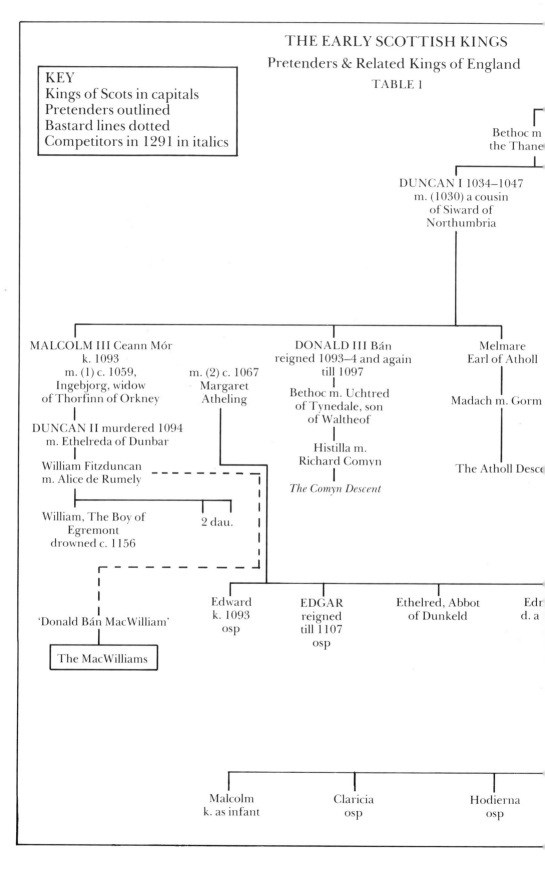

THE EARLY SCOTTISH KINGS
Pretenders & Related Kings of England
TABLE 1

KEY
Kings of Scots in capitals
Pretenders outlined
Bastard lines dotted
Competitors in 1291 in italics

Bethoc m
the Thane

DUNCAN I 1034–1047
m. (1030) a cousin
of Siward of
Northumbria

MALCOLM III Ceann Mór
k. 1093
m. (1) c. 1059,
Ingebjorg, widow
of Thorfinn of Orkney

m. (2) c. 1067
Margaret
Atheling

DONALD III Bán
reigned 1093–4 and again
till 1097

Melmare
Earl of Atholl

DUNCAN II murdered 1094
m. Ethelreda of Dunbar

Bethoc m. Uchtred
of Tynedale, son
of Waltheof

Madach m. Gorm

William Fitzduncan
m. Alice de Rumely

Histilla m.
Richard Comyn

The Atholl Desce

William, The Boy of
Egremont
drowned c. 1156

2 dau.

The Comyn Descent

'Donald Bán MacWilliam'

Edward
k. 1093
osp

EDGAR
reigned
till 1107
osp

Ethelred, Abbot
of Dunkeld

Edr
d. a

The MacWilliams

Malcolm
k. as infant

Claricia
osp

Hodierna
osp

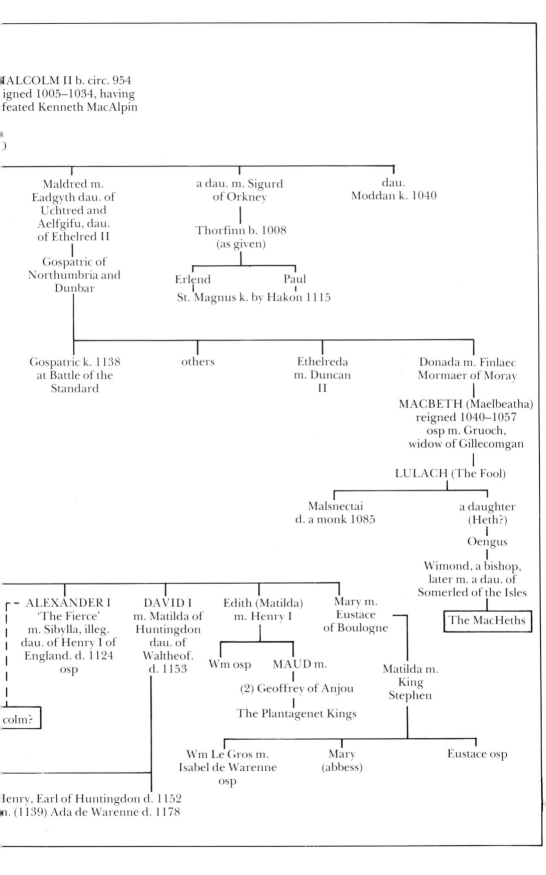

MALCOLM II b. circ. 954
reigned 1005–1034, having
defeated Kenneth MacAlpin

Maldred m.
Eadgyth dau. of
Uchtred and
Aelfgifu, dau.
of Ethelred II

a dau. m. Sigurd
of Orkney

dau.
Moddan k. 1040

Gospatric of
Northumbria and
Dunbar

Thorfinn b. 1008
(as given)

Erlend

Paul

St. Magnus k. by Hakon 1115

Gospatric k. 1138
at Battle of the
Standard

others

Ethelreda
m. Duncan
II

Donada m. Finlaec
Mormaer of Moray

MACBETH (Maelbeatha)
reigned 1040–1057
osp m. Gruoch,
widow of Gillecomgan

LULACH (The Fool)

Malsnectai
d. a monk 1085

a daughter
(Heth?)

Oengus

Wimond, a bishop,
later m. a dau. of
Somerled of the Isles

ALEXANDER I
'The Fierce'
m. Sibylla, illeg.
dau. of Henry I of
England. d. 1124
osp

DAVID I
m. Matilda of
Huntingdon
dau. of
Waltheof.
d. 1153

Edith (Matilda)
m. Henry I

Mary m.
Eustace
of Boulogne

The MacHeths

Wm osp

MAUD m.

Matilda m.
King
Stephen

colm?

(2) Geoffrey of Anjou

The Plantagenet Kings

Wm Le Gros m.
Isabel de Warenne
osp

Mary
(abbess)

Eustace osp

Henry, Earl of Huntingdon d. 1152
m. (1139) Ada de Warenne d. 1178

The Charmed Descent

The Charmed Descent

PAMELA HILL

ROBERT HALE · LONDON

ISBN 0 7090 5614 1

Robert Hale Limited
Clerkenwell House
Clerkenwell Green
London EC1R 0HT

Photoset in North Wales by
Derek Doyle & Associates, Mold, Clwyd.
Printed in Great Britain by
St Edmundsbury Press Ltd, Bury St Edmunds, Suffolk.
Bound by WBC Book Manufacturers Limited,
Bridgend, Mid-Glamorgan.

Author's Note

Among the thirteen Competitors for the Crown of Scotland in 1291 was a certain Robert Pinkeney, claiming to be descended from a bastard daughter of Henry, Earl of Huntingdon. This has been proved to have been chronologically unlikely as well as out of character. As far as is known Earl Henry had no children by anyone except his wife, Ada de Warenne.

P.H.

PART I

One

It was an ill charm. It had already killed two kings. The third, who had been blinded, and who was now a very old man, murmured it to himself in the silence of the laundry at Rescobie, where they had made him work now for twenty years. The charm was his only solace except for the mumbling of a poem in Gaelic that the saint of that race, named Berchan, had made about the old man's dead brother, King Malcolm Ceann Mór, Great Chief and King of Scotia.

> *A king, the best who possessed Alban;*
> *He was a king of kings fortunate.*
> *He was the vigilant crusher of enemies.*
> *No woman bore or will bring forth in the East*
> *A king whose rule will be greater over Alban;*
> *And there shall not be born for ever*
> *One who had more fortune and greatness.*

He himself could have been such a king after his brother, but the Sassunachs had come, and had aided his brother's son by the Sassunach woman and also, a son of the first marriage named Duncan after their father. He himself, third king of the name of Donald, had reigned first of all six months, after expelling the English at court, and then a second time for three years; and had passed a further two, hiding in the forests among the hills, before they caught him in the end and rendered him useless.

He said the charm again. If he recited it often enough, as some said their prayers, it would put one of the new race of kings again in his power. Meantime, there was the linen to be washed. Old Donald shuffled back and forth across the trodden earth floor to fetch water from the deep well there, hauling the rope upwards through his strong hands by feel. His bones ached; the east wind of Forfar was very cold today, blowing as it did straight off the sea. The old man's hair, which had been white in colour even when he was young, stirred lightly, and his unkempt beard with it. There was no sound except for the keening of the wind and the sounds of the murmured Gaelic. This was the tongue he, Donald Bán, loved best, though French and even the Saxon tongue were known to him, he having spent some time in the courts of the south long ago, after his father's murder, in Cnut's time and MacBeth's. He had not liked their ways and had made his way north to the islands, and had spent time there instead.

Later, the son of Cnut's Norman queen by her first marriage had come over and had reigned in England, and had been too holy to get himself an heir; they said King Edward the Confessor would be made a saint in time. The old man's discoloured teeth showed in a wolf's grin beneath his empty eye-sockets. There had been trouble after that in England, and the Sassunach woman and her brother Edgar, who should have had the throne there afterwards but would not fight, had come here in a ship, driven by storm, and the woman had entranced his brother Malcolm with her long golden hair and her southern ways. She had become Malcolm's second wife and had by the end borne him six sons, calling herself holy also. Thinking of Margaret Atheling now, the old blind man spat. It was because of her that the Romish ways of religion had come in, the Lenten fastings and the strict observance of Sunday. By now, he himself never knew which day of the week it was; she and his brother were long dead, having died in different places but almost together. They had taken her body secretly in a mist out of Edinburgh, and had buried it elsewhere, afraid no doubt of his vengeance then. It was however right that the strongest man in a line of kings should inherit and not, in the new Norman fashion, the eldest son, who might be a child or a fool. He, the third Donald, would still be reigning now, well into his eightieth year, like his great ancestor Malcolm II who had died at Glamis, but for that woman's sons. His mind was sound as a bell still, his hands strong to wield a sword; stronger for twenty years of wringing wet linen.

He wrung it now, feeling with scorn its fine quality, brought from the south; shifts for Earl David's delicate lady, fallen in labour upstairs so that they had stopped here, in this remote place where they kept him, instead of riding on to the north for once to see King Alexander, as he called himself; but Alexander's wife had borne no children and there had been ill feeling about the ruling of Lothian. Earl David and his wife had a son already, here with his nurse: one had heard him running about.

The old man grinned again, and the charm in his mind grew swift and evil. A son, and a son's son accursed; young Edgar the second brat, the first having been slain beside Malcolm his father, had called himself king at last with English help and was by now dead mysteriously, they said, after a reign of nine years. Nine was the named number. Edgar they insisted had been sweet and amiable. He had had oneself blinded, but not made a eunuch because of the earlier anointing, on the sacred stone of Scone. Nothing could remove that unction.

Edgar had taken no wife. The sons of Margaret Atheling preferred to live as monks, as she herself would no doubt have preferred to be a nun. Two had become churchmen, one for his sins, for joining with oneself in the second reign of three years there had been: Edmund, dispossessed, had later repented, and they said had asked to be buried in chains; he might be living or dead still in his monastery, one never knew. He, Donald, the first time had seized power alone, had had himself seated and anointed on the sacred place and then had driven out the English who infested his dead brother's houses, including the younger children of the marriage, this Earl David himself and his sisters and Alexander, who was still young then. The hated woman's blood, the royal Saxon blood of Alfred and Cerdic, had seemed banished for all time: but aid had come from the south and the sons had returned as men. There had been young Duncan, Malcolm's son by his first marriage who had reigned, but not for long because oneself had had him killed; he had grown soft with English ways, having been brought up in the south as a hostage from childhood. Six months. The second Duncan's blood had dripped from him at last on the edge of a mormaer's sword; he, Donald, had ordered it, and had made himself king a second time accordingly. The sound of the water dripping from the linen now, as he wrung the wet shifts, reminded him of the thought of the blood. It had been long ago, and Duncan II himself had left a son, but the boy had no fight in him and had been given a Norman name, William Fitzduncan.

Drip, drip; and a second sound, running footsteps, those of the child. Donald's own hearing had become more acute since he was blinded. A child. He had a daughter of his own, safe married long ago in Tynedale; his line would not die out. But this –

The child came nearer, laughing to itself; it was very young, and the nurse not with it. No doubt she was occupied with the woman in labour upstairs. There had been no cries yet from there.

The child came into the laundry, curious at the smell of lye; he was finding out about unknown things. His name was Malcolm after his grandfather. He had only lately learned to walk by himself and was prattling of it to no one in particular. 'Come,' said Donald Bán in Gaelic. 'Come. *Trobhad. A nìs, a nìs.*'

The curse rose strongly in him, the more so in silence. It cast death on all sons' sons. The Atheling line, calling itself the line of Alfred and of Cerdic, was less ancient than his own, the line of Crinan the Thane, dead in the midst of nine and twenty heroes: the line of Erc. Earl David could ride on, with his lady wife when she was delivered, but their son and heir would not kneel beside them in the new church where the Saxon queen was buried beside his brother Malcolm, killed as he had been in battle in Northumbria. Margaret Atheling had died of grief, they said, when she heard: maybe grief would kill the parents of this child, and King Alexander left then with no heir.

'*Trobhad, trobhad. A nìs, a nìs.*'

Little Malcolm came, running and stumbling. He was used to trusting everyone he met. He had never known anything but gentle love, love from his mother, who had never expected to bear a son again at her age; love from his father Earl David, Prince of Cumbria. He saw an old man crouching strangely to greet him, to catch him as he stumbled, to pick him up. He fell into the old man's arms, hearing his own name.

'Malcolm.'

Malcolm smiled, and nestled trustingly against the white beard; it was dirty, but he was given no time to turn away from the smell. Donald Bán, once King of Alban, put his strong hands about the child's neck and wrung it as he would have wrung a chicken's: as he wrung the linen daily. As the same time a great cry came from upstairs; the Countess had again given birth, to a daughter.

In a little while, after certain things had been done, the nurse who should have had charge of little Malcolm, and who had had to act as midwife for the time, remembered her charge, saw that he was missing and came downstairs, not yet anxiously. She found the old man with his long ancient bones huddled over the piled linen and the dead child. His lips moved and he had taken some kind of seizure. The curse had been fulfilled; now it would afflict all generations till the line of the Sassunach woman was wiped out. It was the black curse of the Gael, the curse of Columcille on the sick man's sword, the curse on all of Atheling seed.

The nurse flung her hands over her mouth in horror, but did not scream aloud lest she disturb her mistress. Whatever happened now Earl David would forgive her; he was a merciful man, and loved Christ.

'You must find a priest to shrive them both; the old man will not live long now. Do that first; see that no news reaches my lady yet. I myself will tell her when it is time.'

The Earl's shrewd and kindly face above its soft brown beard was pale with shock and grief. He had taken up the dead child's body in his arms where it lay flaccid, still warm, the head lolling. This should, one day, have been the King of all Scotland. Earl David turned his eyes away from the little congested face and prayed as his mother, whom he barely remembered, had taught him: to forgive one's enemies, to be delivered from evil and to do none. The twitching had meantime stilled, nearby on the floor. It did not matter that both child and old man were dead by now, unshriven; Malcolm had committed no sin in all his short life, and there would be masses said for him and for the old blind deposed king who was a murderer many times over already. He, David, having been taken swiftly to England with the rest after the killings of his father and eldest brother, the death of his mother and the expulsion of half the Court, had clung in his bewilderment to prayer in all things, and the solace of a priest. For the rest of his life masses would be said for the soul of this child, his heir, so dreadfully and soon taken: but also for the soul of Donald Bán, who should be buried with honour as an anointed king, whatever his sins, at Dunkeld among his ancestors. The Earl stared down at the huddle of ancient bones below the grimed white hair. This was his father's brother, last of the old Tanist princes of Alba, and it was partly his, David's, fault, as well as that of his brother Alexander who ruled the northern parts, that they had been busied with affairs and had forgotten, till today, that a prisoner at Rescobie worked over the years, imprisoned, pitiful and blind, washing linen.

He kissed the dead child, turned, still carrying it, and went to give orders for the coffins to be made before going upstairs to break the news to his wife.

*   *   *

Matilda of Northampton, Countess of Huntingdon and Princess of Cumbria, lay with her new daughter by her. She was pleased, and having slept had begun to recover from her earlier tiredness. Although the birth had come sooner than expected, and the agony in her delicate body had as always on such occasions seemed to tear it apart, the child lived and was well formed: small, it is true, but with a skin already clear as a rose. All of the Atheling blood, all of her own inheritance of the beauty of her murdered father Waltheof, was reflected in this flowerlike skin; little Malcolm, whom she would soon kiss again and show him his new sister, had it also. So had her two sons by her first marriage, which had been less happy than this.

She let her mind dismiss that, and the recollection of old Simon de Senlis – St. Liz as they called it here – who had had one leg shorter than the other and would sooner have married her mother, except that Waltheof's widow Judith would have none of him. She, Matilda herself, very young then but an heiress, had been given to him instead: all that was over. The notion came to her that, with the Earl her second husband's agreement now, she would like to name this new child Claricia; it suited her. She looked forward to discussing it with the Earl, pleasantly as they did all things, being happy together although he was seven years her junior and had only been persuaded to marry at all by old King Henry, perhaps against his own inclinations as he had been brought up to revere the Confessor and to remain virgin like most of his brothers had: but then, as the King of England had pointed out, there would be no sons to succeed and what had happened in England in his father the Conqueror's time might happen also in Scotland, with bloodshed resulting. So, although David had been shy with her at first, she had won him, being a widow; perhaps a younger woman – the thought came curiously to her now – would have been less successful. How kind he had been to her at Malcolm's birth, and what joy the little boy had brought to them both! Now he had a sister, and the two could grow up together; it did not matter that this was a girl, her first. It would be pleasant to guide and instruct Claricia, to teach her embroidery, to wear her clothes elegantly; that was important, Alexander's queen Sibylla was criticised for her clumsy gait and the careless throwing on of her clothes, not like the usual elegant Norman habit; Sibylla was a bastard of old King Henry's and no doubt took after her uncle, Robert Curthose, who had waddled to his long fate: but one must not be unkind. Poor Alexander did his best to love Sibylla and had even let her wear his famous pearls, but it made no difference. Also, Sibylla was barren; one could not help but feel a little triumphant, in all charity. Alexander had a bastard son somewhere, it was said by some, called Malcolm also; but he would never rival theirs.

Malcolm. It was an ancient name, meaning, the Earl had told her, Mal-columb, kin to Columba himself by way of Crinan the Thane. King Malcolm Canmore had called none of his sons by his second wife after himself, as he already had three, one so named, by the first; one understood that something unpleasant had happened to them. The Earl kept unpleasantness from her as far as he could, and one did not ask any more.

She began to reflect on the nature of the second husband she had married and whom by now she deeply loved. Earl David was different from his brother Alexander, though both were pious; less given to impulse, gentler – they called Alexander the Fierce up here after he had firmly pursued some rebels across a river in spate in the north, but her husband would after all have done the same if necessary – more shrewd, perhaps; Alexander resented the fact of his dead brother Edgar's partition of the kingdom between them both on his deathbed. At Alexander's death, the land would be one again under her husband, who would rule it as well as his father Malcolm Canmore, even the wild tribes further north; one knew very little about them. Afterwards, after he and she were both gone, Scotland would be Malcolm's, their son's, as king. Already Matilda longed to see her son again, to hold him in her arms, to show him his new sister. Where was he? The place seemed unduly silent; he must have stopped running about for the time, having tired himself out.

'Mald. My love, Mald.'

He called her that; it was the short form of her name, as there were many Matildas, including his own late sister King Henry's Queen, who had been christened Edith but on marriage had taken the name after her mother-in-law, the Conqueror's wife, Matilda of Flanders. She –

'Mald, you must be very brave. It is ill news we must both bear.'

She stared up at him from the bed. Was he disturbed that the child was a girl? The light was behind his head and she could not see his expression. He was speaking for some reason now about King David in the Scriptures, who had lost a child and while it was ill, had covered his head with sackcloth and had mourned, but once it was dead had ceased mourning. What had that to do with them, the story of a dead child? Little Claricia slept sweetly, breathing, a living rose. A dead child. A dead –

'Malcolm.' An accident. No, she must not see him. 'Try to remember him as he was, as you and I loved him, and that we will meet him again before God, when all will again be joy. Try to think of that.' He took her hand, her smooth hand fragrant now with rosewater, that had never done any rougher work than embroidery in its life, and held it. By then the Earl was weeping himself. They wept together.

'What happened?' she said presently. 'I must know. I am strong enough now. If you do not tell me, others will. Tell me of it. Tell me.'

He told her. She was silent for moments. Then she said 'I remember the death of my father Waltheof, Siward's heir. They cut his head off, and held it up by the fair hair, calling him a traitor. My mother, who had helped betray him, never ceased to mourn him, would never again marry though she was niece to the Conqueror and had many offers. All the land wept for him, remembering his beauty. I am not unused to ill tidings. I can bear them.'

She closed her eyes for moments, still holding on to his hand. Then she said 'God willing, my dear lord, if it is the last gift I make you, I will give you another son in the time that is left me. If I die without doing so, you must take another wife.'

'There will be no wife for me but you,' he told her. They sat together for a long time, with his hand still in hers; below, at last, there came the sound of footsteps bearing out the two coffins to the chapel, to rest there till the time of procession to burial.

'I would have buried the murderer outwith the abbey walls.'

So spake Cormac, Bishop of Dunkeld, picking without appetite at his portion of fish. Granted this was a mourning occasion, but it was a fact that the Abbot, Margaret Atheling's remaining son Ethelred, had a say in such matters and a notion of penances, so the fish was stale. Abbot Ethelred, his fair head obediently shaved in the Roman tonsure, meantime wiped his fine fingers with a towel proffered by one of the monks; all of his habits remained princely, and it was difficult to assert one's own authority. The Bishop eased his low-crowned mitre on his head surreptitiously, and scratched the lice therein. It was best to remain silent: this was a king's matter.

Abbot Ethelred – he held the earldom of Fife also, but seldom used the title – looked up now to where his brothers sat; the King, and Earl David, the murdered child's father. Both resembled their common sire King Malcolm more than he, being brown of hair and, in David's case, of beard; Alexander had kept the shaven habit of the Normans of the south. He was silent now as was his wont, but Earl David spoke.

'Donald III may be a murderer, but he was an anointed king. If we forget that, there are those in the north who will remember, and that he endured imprisonment and blindness for many years at our late brother's hands and also ours. In other words we had put him out of our minds, wrongly. That will not be forgiven by the Gaels if they hear of it again now, and that he died working as a servant. For that reason I have brought my son's body quietly here alongside his for burial, rather than creating a stir in Dunfermline itself. My son was too young for many to know of his life: the manner of his death need not be widely spoken of. Many children die young.' His face was grief-stricken as he spoke, but never bitter; he was a man who prayed constantly and remained near God.

'You are prudent,' said a third voice, that of the King of Alban. Alexander and his wife had ridden into Dunkeld from Edinburgh for the burying. Alexander the Fierce did not beseem his name by any notable feature: he was the kind of man who would remain unnoticed in a crowd. He was devout, like his brothers. His exploit in pursuing the northern rebels across the river in spate was remembered by folk as one thing to be certain of. Otherwise he ruled them quietly. He looked across the Abbot's table at his brother the Earl now with something less than liking in his gaze. 'Maybe,' he said carefully, 'it was for the sake of that prudence of yours that our brother King Edgar, God rest his soul, gave you on his deathbed the south part of the kingdom and myself the north, thereby dividing it.'

'Peace, peace,' said their brother the Abbot. 'Do not start that quarrel again. The thing is done, the folk accept it, and both of you rule well. Our brother Edgar maybe knew, young as he was, by then, having ruled himself for nine years, that the whole of Scotia was overmuch for one man, with its many races all with their different ways and customs, Gaels and Picts and

Scots of Lothian and the men of Galloway, Saxons and the rest;
and the murder of our father's son Duncan to recall.'

'They would sooner recall the murder by MacBeth of the
first Duncan, our father's father. The second Duncan the Scots
would deem a Norman, no more. He spent all his youth at the
court of England as a hostage, and married an English bride,
kin to King Ethelred.'

'Well, their son is loyal,' remarked Earl David, whose close
friend William Fitzduncan remained; the man was lecherous,
but otherwise would never betray him.

Abbot Ethelred had fallen silent. 'I remember,' he said
suddenly, 'when we carried our mother's body out from
Edinburgh Castle in the mist God sent in early morning, and
got it safe to Dunfermline. Had the mist not come, Donald's
men would have done it harm.'

They fell to renewed silence, remembering, while the monks
in equal silence removed the remains of the meal, their feet in
leather brogans padding quietly back to the kitchens. The
princely brothers remained, though the Bishop made his
excuses and left. Of the six sons Margaret Atheling in her time
had borne Malcolm Canmore, there were but three now over
whom the tallow lamps flickered from the walls in the growing
dark, their rush wicks burning low by reason of the long talk
there had been. Maybe, as there was not often such a meeting
of them together, three ghosts joined them; that of Edward,
slain at Alnwick with their father over twenty years since and
dying a few hours after him; Edgar the nine years' king, dead at
thirty-three of no man knew what illness; and Edmund the
penitent, buried in his chains in Somerset, where he had fled to
take vows after the defeat of old Donald in the end. There were
sisters too, in absence; King Henry's queen, ailing by now in
England, and the youngest, Mary, mother of children in
Boulogne.

However there were no women present. The new Cistercian
ways prevailed at Dunkeld and unlike the old glad Cluniac
hospitality, they ate separately in a different part of the
building if they were entertained at all. None of Margaret's
sons having married except two, only two were with the party;
Sibylla, Alexander's queen, who was one of old King Henry's
many bastards out of England – her brother had escorted them
here today and sat now lower down the table – and Mald
herself, sick with grief, who had eaten nothing and lay on the
guest-house pallet, her beads in her fingers. She was thinking,

and knew Earl David would be thinking also, of their child's little body, alone in the candlelit dark.

However Sibylla, Queen of Alban, had partaken unwillingly of the stale fish. It made her impatient, as she was fond of food. She knew that she had lost what looks she had ever had by eating too much, but by now had no other interests, though she went through the motions of piety by Alexander's side. He had been made to marry her by her overpowering father, who wanted all his bastards married well; another was a princess in Wales, another in Man and yet another in Galloway. Sibylla discounted the rest; there were twenty altogether, as King Henry's attentions had strayed both before and after the marriage with his pious queen.

Sibylla yawned, and thought instead of the journey she and her husband would shortly make, as they were here in any case, to visit the monks of Loch Tay. It was a favourite place of hers; the fish, if one had to eat it, was fresh caught from the loch, and there was game from the hills, properly hung; they kept a good table there. This place was unspeakable, unfit for persons of rank. Sibylla fingered her matchless freshwater pearls, which the King permitted her to wear; they were famous and she had not discarded them for the mourning. Often she would see Alexander looking at their soft sheen and would know that he was thinking not of herself but of his mother; the name Margaret meant a pearl. He did not, come to that, think often of her, Sibylla, and never now lay with her as there was no purpose in it, she having borne no children. No doubt she was too fat. In any case – she shrugged, remembering – he had always scourged himself afterwards and had gone to confession. Once, he had confessed to her at the beginning, he had got a son on a young woman in the west. Well, other men had done the same; but it showed that the barrenness was her fault and not his. Well, there was no help for that. Perhaps Mald would bear Earl David more children, despite her age.

Sibylla fished in her purse, which swung in the ordinary way at the hem of her gown, and, keeping her head turned away lest Mald see, extracted a sweetmeat. It was a kind she favoured, made of pounded Spanish almonds and honey, and took away the taste of the late fish. They could at least have disguised that with lavender, and had not.

In the abbey itself, candles burned in the shadows, at head and foot of the new tombs, that of the old man and the child. Surrounding them were the graves of all their ancestors who had died before King Malcolm Ceann Mór had built, at his wife's request, the new great chapel at Dunfermline, where they themselves were buried. Here, now, lay all of the House of Dunkeld who were not buried on Iona: all who had ruled in Alban in old time back to the MacAlpin kings; and even they had come to power by the murder of seven men at a feast. There was evil remembered in the darkness, but the lamp of the sanctuary burned; and presently Earl David came alone, and knelt to pray for his son's soul before going to his wife.

Soon, before King Alexander's death in a year or two – he did not make old bones any more than the rest – a man and woman and their little girl were brought to Earl David. They were not of common stock, as could be seen from the way the man – and he himself was Uchtred the son of Waltheof, Mald's father – upheld his wife's hand respectfully on his wrist, in the Tanist fashion of regarding women as of equal importance, the makers of kings. She herself was a dignified person, not young; she might have been between thirty and forty years of age, it was difficult to tell; with the little girl, evidently an only child, perhaps ten. Her husband let her speak for herself in Gaelic.

'I am Bethoc, only child of the late King Donald,' she said. 'It was great harm that he did to you, but great harm was likewise done to him. We have come, my husband and I, from Tynedale to ask you, and maybe King Alexander if we must journey further, to let me take my father's bones from Dunkeld and bury them again on Iona, with the old kings in the Ard Rí, the ancient row of carved stones. If you will do this for me, I in turn will do a thing for you.' She brought forward the child. 'This is my daughter Histilla, and I will leave her with you to be married in time to anyone you yourself may choose, for you are a son of Margaret Atheling and will be king in your turn like the rest, and it is a long time now since the son of a daughter inherited, in the old way.' She smoothed the child's hair. 'I myself can bear no more children,' she said. 'Let me have my father's bones to do them honour, and then Histilla's sons shall do the like to you when their day comes.'

'I may not see that day myself,' said Earl David; none of his brothers had lived long and Alexander was already ailing.

'Ah, you will live to be old. You will be a great king, and will have a son, and he will have sons to follow him. I have a little of the Sight in my blood; my great-great-grandfather was the second Malcolm who lived to be very old, and I have the blood of Siward in me also, and he was descended from a fairy. It is not wise to laugh at such things.'

Earl David laid his hands on the little girl's head, and said a blessing: she gazed up at him with great eyes. This was the Tanist heiress, whose sons would have reigned as kings of the ancient way in Alban. In barter for old Donald's bones Histilla was a good bargain, and Earl David was not without bargaining power in such matters. He thought at once of a possible bridegroom for her; one of the young grandsons of Robert de Comines, a Fleming of the Conqueror's who had been killed last century in Northumbria fighting one's father. His son John was however loyal, and remained such about oneself since the early days at King Henry's court when David's sister, the good queen, had been still alive: she had died lately. Earl David smiled.

'You may do as you wish with your father's body,' he said to her. 'I myself will see that my brother the King knows of it; you need journey no further.'

Bethoc's face shone: it was curious that it should mean so much to her, for the father in question she could surely not remember, having been got by old Donald while he was a fugitive at the onset, even then, of old age. It was tradition that mattered, to the Gaels; David knew it already, and it would aid him in governing them when the time came. Bethoc began to chant now in the way they had, reciting all the names of the former kings who lay beneath the carved stones on Columba's sacred island; Lulach the Fool, MacBeth's stepson, MacBeth himself, the first and second Duncan, all the rest.

'This one must lie under a flat stone that he may not rise again,' grunted Uchtred of Tynedale, evidently unwilling to have come on this journey in order to part with his only daughter; but his wife no doubt ruled him by reason of her descent. In any case David told the couple to take their child back with them till she should be older, when he would find her a good knight suitable to her birth. He did not mention the Comyns, as they now called themselves, yet. He would have kept the child Histilla as hostage, as was common, but the constant presence about his court of a young granddaughter of old Donald Bán would remind his wife of the child she herself had lost, and she was already expecting another; as for Claricia, she was still too young to need a companion.

Two

In the following year the Countess gave birth to a second girl, and this time wept with disappointment. Her body, which had never been strong and was no longer young, was exhausted; this was her fifth child, Earl David's third. Since the killing of little Malcolm she had lost all pleasure in life: she clung to her two daughters, refusing to let the children out of her sight. What if she failed in her promise to bear another son, and still did not die? But the Earl comforted her.

'The two little girls are your solace; have no fear, they will grow up as companions to one another, being so close of an age.'

'They shall never marry. They shall never leave me.'

He looked grave, but did not reproach her: it was according to his own inclinations. Margaret Atheling had brought up her own two daughters, Edith and Mary, with the intention of making them nuns; one day his father King Malcolm had broken out in a rage at the sight of young Edith already in a nun's veil, had torn it off her head and trampled on it, saying no daughter of his should ever take vows. Edith had not, despite pressure all her youth from her aunt Christina who was abbess of Romsey, and Edith had married King Henry instead; but his unfaithfulness had made her most unhappy, and perhaps all things considered she would have been better in the cloister. 'As you will,' her husband said to Mald now gently. 'Nevertheless this is the child of today; let us love her, and call her Hodierna.' It was a name his sister Mary, married after all in Boulogne, had told him of as being common enough in Flanders.

Knowing it might be the will of God that he should never have a son, Earl David cherished the two little girls and let them stay close to their mother. In the meantime Queen Sibylla, Alexander's wife, died suddenly near remote Loch Tay. She had been one of King Henry's numerous bastards, certainly, all

22

of whom he had married off well; but she had not been a suitable bride for a King of Scots, and Alexander had been talked into it. David earnestly tried to persuade his brother to marry again for the sake of the kingdom, but Alexander would not; he said he was not well, wanted to be left in peace, and seemed sunk in pious exercises for the welfare of Sibylla's soul; they had made several endowments together. A childless king, and the heir with daughters only; well, it was the same situation as little Histilla's in Tynedale, soon to marry Comyn. Earl David bided his time. One could only pray that some solution would be sent by God.

It was sent. Mald came to him, trembling, saying that she was again with child. 'I am forty-five years old,' she reminded him. 'I would gladly die in giving your son birth. Pray therefore that it may be a son.'

It was a son, and she did not die, although he was brought into the world with great agony. He was a beautiful child, but not as strong as Malcolm had been. They called him Henry, after the King of England his uncle by marriage; but he did not in the least resemble that portentous and licentious monarch, who made his courtiers quail and who by now snored greatly as he slept. Young Henry looked instead like the Athelings and Earl Waltheof, Mald's unforgotten father, with their delicate skin and fair hair, and the features and disposition of an angel. In fact, Henry of Huntingdon was almost too good to be true: perhaps it could be excused him, considering everything. He was sent, when he was old enough, to Roxburgh to be educated with his two half-brothers, Mald's sons by her earlier marriage, Simon and Waldef, as the name was spelt by now; also a boy of his own age named Ailred, who from the beginning adored him.

By the time young Henry of Scotland was christened, King Henry of England had himself suffered, vicariously, from the ill charm. His Atheling wife, David's sister, was dead, and the memory of her washings of the feet of lepers and her charities had earned her the name of Good Queen Maud; a daughter was married long ago in Germany, the son and heir, William, newly married at home. In a disaster in the Channel the White Ship, crossing over from Normandy on a maiden voyage, foundered on a rock and sank with all aboard, including Prince William and his little-known brother Richard, but not his bride, who had sailed safely with King Henry in the Conqueror's old craft. The bride entered a convent for grief; King Henry himself, having heard the tale from the single member of the lost ship's crew who had clung to the mast and saved himself, was inconsolable, and moreover blamed himself at last for his sins; the Prince had been safe in a small boat about to row off, when one of his bastard half-sisters had called out to him from the sinking ship, begging him to turn back and save her; this had been attempted, the boat had turned back, capsized amid disaster, and all had gone down: the captain had been drunk. All was lost of King Henry's Scots marriage, Atheling wife and children and heirs: the once proud man became a misanthrope, and married again of necessity soon, a young girl from Brabant who should have borne him children but for whatever reason did not. There was barrenness everywhere, and loss of hope, in England now; could anyone have ill-wished the Atheling blood? But Henry of Scotland, soon to be Earl of Huntingdon, flourished and grew stronger, and his mother was finally persuaded not to keep him, like the girls, forever at her side, but to allow him to be made a man.

King Alexander the Fierce died then, having remained a widower for four years. Earl David was King of all Scotia at last, and was anointed at the sacred place of Scone, on the stone which was said to have been Jacob's pillow long ago at Bethel. In England the troubles increased; a woman had never been known to reign, and the sole heir to King Henry, the Conqueror's son, now, was his sole legitimate daughter, widowed of her old German Emperor: the Empress Maud, and her temper was not easy. She had been married again, by her father's wish rather than hers, to a much younger husband than herself, named Geoffrey of Anjou.

King David set meantime about his strong wise rule. He was to build nine abbeys in his time, and the first was at Jedburgh. His Queen lived quietly on; many thought Matilda of Huntingdon dead within seven years, but she lived instead for more than twenty to sign a charter at the last. However she was a pale shadow now, her duty done. King David never ceased to love her, and at her death had her buried not at Dunfermline, where his parents lay entombed, but at Scone itself, where he and Mald had received their anointing together; it was not yet the fashion, as in England, to include a crown.

Three

Ada de Warenne carefully replaced her needle in the silk. The swaying of the litter made it inadvisable to continue sewing bride-clothes or anything else; she might either prick her finger, and bleed on to the work, or else lose the silver needle itself among the cushions: and there might well be delay, in Scotland, in procuring another: one never knew. To arrive with a reasonably filled dower-chest was however important, and the marriage had been arranged in such haste by Queen Matilda, with the Earl, Ada's brother, imprisoned by King Stephen, that there had not been enough time to fit Ada herself out suitably. Not only would Earl Henry of Huntingdon, her bridegroom, one day be King of Scots, but the de Warenne family were related both to the Kings of England and of France. It would not do to appear other than suitably dressed for one's position on arrival.

The chest itself swayed meantime, attached securely, as one hoped, between the wooden wheel-struts, which lurched more than ever now that the ways had grown less smooth up here on the moors where even the Romans had not penetrated. Ada set the sewing aside and moved the curtain cautiously to see a little more of the landscape. This was certainly very wild and strange, with crows pecking here and there at carrion still remaining after the late battle at Clitheroe: but safer than most of England at present. Besides, Reynald her second brother and Ralph the third, and their following, were escorting her, and Adelia Reynald's wife – poor imprisoned Will's shrew of a Countess had thankfully stayed at home in Lewes – was here in the litter, having fallen asleep at the further end with her mouth open. It was in fact seldom closed; Adelia chattered without ceasing when she was awake, and the quiet now was restful, with only the clatter of the armoured escort heard beyond the curtain, and voices when there were any. One had heard enough about Poynton, pleasant as it was, and Adelia

25

and Reynald's children left behind there meantime in the new wooden dwelling by the lake. Adelia's forebears the Mowbrays had fought at Hastings, and she was therefore proud; but so had one's own. Grandfather, the first William de Warenne out of Normandy, had married the Conqueror's daughter Gundreda, who had later died in childbirth before William himself became the first Earl of Surrey. Ada's own elder sister Gundred had not come, any more than Countess Ela; Gundred was no doubt busy quarrelling with her second husband exactly as she had done with the first.

Ada herself had come over as a stranger to them all, except for Ralph, having been reared in the latter's company at Bellencombre, the old castle in Normandy which looked down on the river Varenne, from which the family took its name since time immemorial; in Latin – Ada had been taught a little, and could write – the name was the Varemna. De Varennes, or de Warennes as they called it now in England, had lived beside the river since Bronze Age times. Then the Danes had sailed down to France, and Danish blood had mingled with French along the coasts to make Norman; and old Herfast the Dane, the first William de Warenne's great-grandfather, had been own brother to lovely Duchess Gunnor of Normandy herself, wife to Duke Richard the Fearless and grandmother to Edward the Confessor by their daughter's marriage to King Ethelred. That was all very long ago, and the Conquest had come between; but it was possible to have admired, in a detached way and without too much awe, the handsome prince who had come from Scotland to Westminster some years back, when Ada herself, then very young, had been visiting Lewes for her mother's funeral. Earl Henry of Huntingdon had sat at King Stephen's right hand, and had had angelic beauty and, they whispered, all the virtues both of a prince and a monk. That was before the Archbishop of Canterbury and the Earl of Chester had shouted insults, and the Prince of Scotland, which Earl Henry was, had been taken away. Ralph had made an earthy comment when, after the second battle which the Scots had lost, Queen Matilda had arranged, for the sake of peace between the two lands, that Ada herself would make Henry of Huntingdon a suitable bride. 'Bride to a monk?' Ralph had jeered; they were good friends. 'You will have to instruct him, my sister; not that you know any more about the business than he does.'

Well, she knew enough, perhaps, to instruct Earl Henry if it should be needed, although her mother, who could have told her more, had died when she was ten. As for her father, the second Earl, Ada had seen very little of him; not only had he been in constant trouble, and prison often, for backing first one of the Conqueror's warring sons on the wrong side and then the other, but also for loving, all his life, the woman whom Henry, the third and youngest son of the Conqueror, who had become King of England in the end, had chosen to marry. Good Queen Maud had been beyond the second Earl's reach from youth, but he had never loved any other woman; certainly not the young widow he eventually wedded, though Isabel de Vermandois, Countess of Leicester and already mother of sons, was kin to the King of France. There had been children of the second marriage and Ada herself was one; but Countess Isabel had always preferred young Leicester and the Beaumonts, fruit of her first and happier union. So Ralph had related: Ralph in some fashion heard everything. At any rate, he had said, Good Queen Maud would have been hard to live up to, with her washings of the feet of lepers and the like; no wonder King Henry's attentions had strayed; he had twenty bastards, as everyone knew, and had married all of them very well. One, Sibylla, had until lately been Queen in Scotland, but now was dead.

At any rate, the royal English marriage had been wasted, because in the White Ship disaster after her death King Henry had lost his legitimate heir by Maud, and had become thereafter grave and ponderous: he had married again soon, a pretty young princess from Louvain, but Adelicia had borne him no children, although now, with a second marriage for love of her own after Henry's death, there were several. There had been no one, therefore, to inherit the throne of England except for Henry and Maud's daughter, the younger Maud, married at twelve to the old Emperor of Germany. He had died, and the Empress, by then in her late twenties, had been made by the King her father to marry a young man named Geoffrey of Anjou, very handsome but only fifteen at the time. They whispered that the son born five years later had not been Geoffrey's at all, but on the contrary King Stephen's; and Stephen, her own cousin from Blois, had meantime seized Maud's throne. So there was war in England, not only by reason of that but because King Stephen, affable and handsome host as he was, could not control his barons. Several of the castles they had passed over the past few days on the way north had been built without licence, and reared grimly on their mottes; it was said unspeakable things happened in them. Ada, who was not given to lack of courage, had been glad of her escort.

She thought of King Stephen now, and of his kindly queen, who was herself the niece of King David of Scotland and, therefore, her bridegroom Earl Henry's cousin. Queen Matilda and Earl Henry had met at Durham after the disastrous Battle of the Standard, during which Earl Henry himself had saved the Scots cavalry, and had arranged this marriage as a way of making peace; after all, the two royal houses were related and it was absurd to be at war. She, Ada, descended from the Conqueror, would help to atone for the awkwardness, as King David had taken a vow to support his niece the Empress Maud against King Stephen: and would also, it was hoped, solace the hurt pride of Earl Henry himself at having been recalled by his father from Westminster that time long ago when the Archbishop and the Earl had publicly insulted him as a foreigner and had said he had no business to be sitting on the King's right hand. It all seemed a great deal of trouble about nothing; but that was the way of men.

A little wind had arisen and the azure Mowbray banner – Adelia made a point of displaying it although few families yet troubled to do so – flapped against the litter's frame, wakening Reynald's wife. The latter stretched, yawned, and began at once to talk again while surveying, beneath her eyelids, the young bride opposite. Reynald's unknown sister from Normandy would bear children easily, Adelia decided, more so than herself; God alone knew the pains of labour for a delicate woman! This girl was big-boned and healthy, sensible at least if not beautiful; her bridegroom, whom one had heard had almost been killed by a grappling-iron some time ago at the siege of Ludlow, except that King Stephen had chivalrously rescued him in time, would himself no doubt provide the beauty; he was almost too perfect in appearance for a man, golden-haired and fine-complexioned and fine-featured. He was, of course, descended from Earl Waltheof, whom nobody in England had forgotten even yet; and, naturally, the Athelings. Most of Queen Margaret Atheling's sons had taken monkish vows, without doubt at her behest; it had evidently not been considered desirable by them to marry, but how was the succession otherwise to continue? Adelia shrugged; her own husband Reynald made no bones about continuing his in the usual way, and Poynton was filled with young voices, and another on the way. She would be glad to return, following this wedding; and to leave poor young Ada to her fate in the north. No doubt the girl would be happy enough once her bridegroom had ceased to be monkish: she seemed placid, and listened rather than talking, always a good thing for any young woman. The prospect of comforting a nervous bride would not have been one Adelia relished, in especial at the moment, when she was feeling somewhat queasy. Ah, to be home again at Poynton, and the lake teeming with fresh fish! It had been an excellent notion to decide to live in Cheshire, removed from the troubles.

Ada became aware that the landscape was changing and flattening, broadening out to where a plain lay and, beyond it, a broad river like the sea. Above was a walled town; Carlisle. Along the way there had begun already to be curious people, the commons, gathered to see the bride sent north for Earl Henry. Ada smiled, though it was not possible for them to see her easily past the escort with its mounted cavalry and flapping banners. She knew an instant's regret that the de Warenne dragon was not to the fore instead of Adelia's lions, but Earl William in prison had been unable to order such things and, after all, it was unimportant. She lay back on her cushions and stared at the folk of Cumbria and the wild Galloway men from across the water, with their long hair and beards and eelskin sword-belts, different from any to be seen in the south; some called blessings in what one supposed was Gaelic; she must perhaps try to learn it. They entered the town within its wall, and were welcomed by the dignified and kindly figure of the King of Scots, greying of hair and beard now and grave since his wife's increasing illness; the Queen herself was not there, but two pale princesses were, who stared at Ada's clothing rather than at her face. The bridegroom, Earl Henry, welcomed Ada's brothers, who descended with the usual great clatter from the saddle, and knelt to the King; then Ada herself was handed out, knelt also, and received on her cheek King David's kiss and then Earl Henry's; but the latter, although he still looked exactly like an angel, kept his eyes cast down. Before Ada was taken away by the women, Ralph whispered in her ear.

'Have no fear, my sister, we'll ply him with wine in time. Good fortune attend you.'

He winked, and saw her off. The lady who took foremost charge, as the Queen was too ill to be present, was evidently named Alice Fitzduncan, and like oneself was a Norman; that was a comfort, until it was discovered that William Fitzduncan himself was considered by many to be the rightful heir to Scotland, and had a young son also named William, who was present today from Egremont. Ada smiled at young William, who returned the smile; he did not look as if he would cause trouble, and his father seemed loyal to the King. Also among the courtiers was one Uchtred of Galloway, a hostage. She would learn the more extraordinary names as time went on. Meantime, it was time to be dressed for her wedding, after which there would be a great feast in the hall. Ada remembered Ralph's promise to ply Earl Henry with wine. Perhaps, however, it would be a little unkind to make him entirely drunk. She herself was not after all without attractions; and went at last to the altar with confidence, seeing there, waiting, the angel's figure waiting of the prince she had come here to marry.

The marriage and feasting were over and the couple had been escorted to bed. Earl Henry knelt in prayer for what Ada considered too long a time, but she waited in silence. Presently, as if unwillingly, he climbed in with her. She turned to him, smiling; one must make such a person feel at ease.

'Carlisle seems a very good walled town,' she said.

'Yes. My father the King acquired it some little time back from King Stephen despite Earl Ranulf of Chester, who said it was his. It is more convenient than Dunfermline, and is nearer my friend Ailred at Rievaulx, who is now a monk there.' He sounded desolate. His French was a very little altered in accent from her own, as though the sea between was like a sword: but they understood one another.

Ada had heard enough about Ailred and monks; she was anxious to make this most beautiful husband look at her as she already looked at him. He had not done so even in course of the marriage ceremony, having kept his eyes down even while they exchanged rings. As for herself, they had combed out her hair again carefully, after the feasting, and had made certain that her skin was fragrant with rosewater; she knew that she looked as well in this her marriage-bed as she had ever looked in all her life. What was the use of that if Henry of Huntingdon would neither look at her nor enjoy the fragrance, and evidently regarded marriage as a duty to be endured rather than as a pleasure to be savoured, at least at the beginning? She must talk to him, again, meantime of other things.

'You have many friends,' she said, dismissing Ailred. 'I myself hardly know anyone in England or here. I have spent most of my life in Normandy, at Bellencombre.' A sudden longing for the familiar place rose in her, and her eyes filled, unusually, with tears; this place was a long way from home. She recalled another stranger at the wedding feast; a stocky freckled bullnecked boy with red hair and large neglected hands which had stuffed his meat anyhow into his mouth; he had assessed her with hard unchildlike eyes. If *he* were a man, and here with her now, he would have taken her already without further words. He was, she had learned, young Henry FitzEmpress, the Lady of England's son, who had been sent to shelter with his uncle in Scotland meantime. Nobody knew what would happen next in England. The boy's grandfather had after all been old King Henry who had, once in Normandy, been lectured by a cleric because he and his courtiers looked like he-goats with their long hair and beards, grown to please the Saxons and Henry's Atheling queen. By then, King Henry had stopped pleasing his queen quite as much and had had himself shaved at once, and his courtiers also. Henry of Huntingdon now was clean-shaven; being fair he no doubt did not need to shave often in any case.

He had looked up for the first time when Ada said she knew nobody. His eyes were beautiful and strange, and perceived her tears. 'Do not be afraid,' he said softly. 'You will make friends soon; there are my sisters, and the King my father is a kindly man, much loved.'

'And you? You are the man I have married, not your father.' She tried not to let her voice grow sharp. She must win him; if it did not happen now, it never would.

'I did not intend to marry,' Henry said then shyly. 'My friend Ailred and I had vowed to remain virgin. He went with many tears into the monastery, but he felt the call of God too strongly to resist and remain with me.'

'Well, you may serve God yourself by caring for your kingdom; look at what has happened in England because the late King Henry left no son behind. There is only one way of making sons, my lord. I am a virgin also: am I so ugly?' She made herself sound downcast; it was evidently best to arouse his pity, as she had done when she said she knew nobody here.

'You are not ugly at all,' he said. His hand reached out and tentatively, almost fearfully, touched her hair, then her naked shoulder. 'No, you are not ugly at all.'

'Then let us make our son. You had a little brother who was killed as a child; I heard of it in Normandy. Let us call our son after him. That will please your father, and the Queen.'

'Yes. We will have a son, perhaps. If so, we will name him Malcolm.' He touched her breast.

During the night, after they had lain together, he asked her among other things how she had come by her own name: he had not heard of it before. By then, she was more sure of him: and answered proudly.

'I was called after a sister of Charlemagne. I am descended from him and from the great Alfred, as you are yourself; Matilda of Flanders, old William's queen, was Alfred's own daughter's descendant by the second Count Baldwin. My grandmother Gundreda was the Conqueror's daughter by Matilda, and though they say she was the youngest, she was the eldest, born before the Papal sanction, like Curthose and Rufus, so that King Henry the third son was the better able to claim the crown of England, as he was born there after the sanction came. I am talking a great deal, my husband, but it is only in order that you may have no fear that our son will have low-born blood in him.' She lay back, triumphant; but he turned away for instants and in the darkness, she could not see his face.

'Then you,' he said slowly, 'are part Atheling also. It is perhaps not a good thing.'

Next day, everyone crowded in to know how the bridal night had sped. Foremost among them was Reynald's wife Adelia, who as the bride's sister-in-law considered herself to have somewhat more of a right to enquire than these wild folk who spoke a variety of tongues besides French. She had sympathy for Reynald's young sister, so soon to be left without succour among them; but Ada seemed cheerful enough.

'You must visit us whenever you ride south,' Adelia said. 'It is less far from here to Poynton than, I believe, to the furthest extent of this kingdom.' The bounds of *that*, up to Moray and Ross, were beyond her understanding. Down here, matters were perhaps a little more familiar; she had been talking yesterday to one of the guests, a young married woman from Morpeth whose father, Earl Gospatric of Dunbar, had died among great slaughter last year at the Battle of the Standard, as they called it because of the raised Host. The young woman's

name was Juliana and her blood was high, in fact the blood of
King Ethelred himself: to find it so far north! That had, of
course, been the first marriage of the beloved, but useless, king
before he espoused Emma of Normandy and fathered King
Edward the Confessor and Edward's murdered brother Alfred
the Atheling: unspeakable things had happened in those days,
exactly as now. She and Juliana had discussed ancestry, which
tended by now to become a trifle confused; but it was clear that
King Ethelred's son by the first marriage had been Edmund
Ironside, dead mysteriously while still young, and he had been
the grandfather of Queen Margaret Atheling who had married
King Malcolm Canmore; there, one had it straightened out at
last. Adelia stowed it all away in her shallow coffer of a mind,
there to lie. She and Reynald would of course return to Poynton
and the children at once. Ralph, on the other hand, being close
to Ada, would stay for a little while, being free to come and go as
he would. He showed no signs of going on crusade, like the
eldest brother, poor William, now released from prison. No
doubt William, third earl, had taken the cross with relief thereafter in order to escape from his shrew of a de Bellesme wife.
However if he did not return, there was only a little daughter left
to inherit the de Warenne and Surrey title; a pity.

Henry of Huntingdon was a young man who might well have
suffered from being, as was natural enough, the apple of his
mother's eye. Constantly fearful and anxious as she had been
lest anything happen to him, his father had wisely taken him
away early from her and from the two girls Claricia and
Hodierna, who were hardly ever permitted to leave the
Queen's side. Henry had been sent instead to be educated with
his two older half-brothers, Mald's sons of her first marriage
Simon and Waldef, at Roxburgh, and young Ailred from
Hexham, who was Henry's own age, had joined them and the
two had grown up together. But Henry had been taught the
arts of war as well as book-learning and devotion, likewise
courtly manners and diplomacy. One of the first testings of the
latter had been when he was still less than twenty years old and
had proudly been sent, as his father's representative, to the
court of King Stephen at Westminster, partly to ensure – it
seemed at that time as if Stephen was certain after all of the
English crown – to ensure the continued holding by the Scots of
the great and important Honour of Huntingdon; King David
was shrewd. He himself had taken, however, a vow to support

his niece Maud as heiress of England, so prudently held aloof. 'You will be careful,' he said to his son, 'to do homage for nothing except Huntingdon.'

Homage apart, young Henry had been shocked by the state of things as he rode south through the land: it was different from anything one could imagine in well-governed Lothian. England, even in sprawling Huntingdon, seemed one great tract of desolation and war: castles reared grimly which had been built without leave, the common people suffered unspeakably, and it was said everywhere that, for lack of a strong king in England, God and his saints slept. Henry did what he could for them on the way; and later had sat in handsome King Stephen's hall, having been made welcome by him and his kindly queen, who was Henry's own cousin, her mother having been Mary, younger daughter of Margaret Atheling who had in her time married Count Eustace of Boulogne. However all had not been smooth; Henry had watched incredulously while the Archbishop of Canterbury rose and shouted insults and old Ranulf of Chester, who had a grudge anyhow about losing Carlisle, clamoured likewise, flinging themselves out thereafter from the King's presence – after all, Stephen had had himself anointed – and one's own. Immediately, King David, Henry's father, hearing of the insult, had demanded Henry's return: and he, therefore, had ridden again out of Westminster with cheeks flaring crimson for shame. Later, his father had made war, partly for that and partly on account of the vow he had earlier sworn to honour his niece the Empress Maud as Lady of England; and there had been the feel of a horse gripped between one's knees, the Dragon of Wessex waving, and the cry of 'Albanach! Albanach!' in one's ears from the Gaels and the men of Galloway, who had won a small victory already at Clitheroe and done much slaughter there, and it had made them wild for blood. That was why the battle had been lost, with Malise of Strathearn himself leading them in their folly of attacking cavalry on foot without armour; and somebody had at last held up a bloodily severed head and called out that it was that of the King of Scots. He, Henry, had turned his own cavalry then in time and had ridden back among the pursuing English, who thought they were accompanied by more of their own knights; and so had won to safety, even saluting the Host raised on a ship's mast in a cart of the enemy's side, to discover King David not dead after all, but still fighting. Nevertheless it had been a rout for Scotland, and a victory for Stephen, and old Robert de Brus of Annandale, who had begged the King with tears at the beginning not to fight, had been justified after all even if he was only thinking of his own extensive lands in England. One way and another, Henry himself had used his diplomacy again later at Durham, where he and Stephen's gallant plump little Queen Matilda had met and had arranged this marriage of his to try to patch everything up between everyone. Before the bride had come, the thought of Ada de Warenne had not been entirely welcome; not only was there the vow he himself had sworn with Ailred never to break, but Ada de Warenne's sister Gundred was married to Warwick, a Beaumont known to be Stephen's man, and her brother's allegiance had also wavered and so, in his time, had her father the second earl's between Curthose and Rufus and their brother King Henry.

However, by now it did not matter, except for the instant's unease he had himself felt with regard to the old blind King Donald's curse. Ada herself seemed strong, placid and sensible, not like his fading sisters who clung always to their mother, ivy round a dying tree. Ada would bear him sons, as she promised; surely some of them would live to reign. There was however still the thing of which his sister Hodierna had reminded him, on hearing that he was to be married, her peaked face peering upwards like a witch's: she was not well, the pair of them never were. They had the wasting illness to which he himself had once almost succumbed, but a monk named Malachy had come from Ireland to cure him, and had laid his hands on him and had then gone on to Clairvaux to die himself at last in the arms of Abbot Bernard, who said Malachy would be made a saint in time.

'If you have sons,' had said Hodierna, 'they will be accursed. The old blind King Donald cursed us all. We will all die young, and so will they.'

She had turned away then, and for the same reason he himself had turned away, briefly, last night from Ada his wife. Perhaps however the curse would not prevail altogether, and some of their sons would live to be old.

Four

Ralph de Warenne stayed with his sister and her new Scots husband for a little while, then went off wherever he was going next, and all of it happened before Ada found herself at last pregnant by Earl Henry. However it was within the year, and they and the King were pleased. Meantime she did her best to cultivate Henry's sisters, but never really achieved it; they were wrapped up in the idea of death beside their mother, while Ada on the contrary was preparing for new life within herself. She found Alice Fitzduncan – Alice had been a de Rumely before her marriage – more congenial. The Fitzduncan heir William had been sent back to his tutors at Egremont, while his parents stayed on at Court. Alice's husband was the son of Malcolm Canmore's eldest son by his first wife Ingebjorg, who had reigned briefly in Scotland for six months before old Donald Bán had him murdered; and that seemed to be the end of it, except that the dead Duncan II himself had been brought up at the English court as a hostage and had acquired soft English ways, as they called them here, which was perhaps why he had been murdered as easily as he had. His son, Alice's husband William, was fiercely loyal to King David and had urged the latter on against the advice of old Robert de Brus to fight after all at the Battle of the Standard, about which Ada was already a little tired of hearing; it was over, after all, and King David was evidently better at ruling his own kingdom than fighting on behalf of others. Nevertheless he had taken the Empress's son young freckled Henry under his wing for the time, but soon the boy's Angevin father Geoffrey Plantagenet – they called him that because he wore a sprig of broom, *planta genista*, in his cap by habit when out hunting, but otherwise seemed an unpleasant person – sent for him, and he left the Scottish Court to settle down in its own new-found peace.

As she thickened, Ada found her marriage becoming increasingly happy; it was evident that Earl Henry trusted her and was beginning to love her. They both knew that his sisters would die, also their mother; all three ailing women had taken themselves, or rather had been taken, back to Dunfermline. Henry had told Ada at last, falteringly, of the ancient curse; with her robust common sense she had made light of it. Nevertheless, there was no doubt that things did not go well for heirs of the Atheling line: there was the tale of Prince William drowned in the White Ship, and later on Prince Eustace, Stephen's son, was to die of choking after setting fire to a monks' cornfield at Bury; well, there it was, and one must see that one's own sons were brought up not to tempt fortune in such ways. 'There is a curse on the Angevins as well,' she assured Henry, 'because old Count Fulk burnt his wife alive at the stake in her wedding dress, and before that there was a fairy named Melusine who vanished with a smell of brimstone through the window at the Elevation when her husband made her stay in church. It is as well not to believe everything, or we would all run mad.'

Henry of Huntingdon smiled. She lightened his somewhat habitual melancholy. He was beginning to be very fond of Ada. If only the birth proved safe!

It was safe. Ada gave birth with ease to the most beautiful boy who was ever born, even more beautiful than his father: and as they had promised one another to do they called him Malcolm. He had fair hair, like the Athelings and dead Waltheof, and a skin like a rose. A little over a year later, a second boy was born to them and called William after Ada's family. William would never be beautiful; he was a Norman, and from the time of his bringing forth he waved his big square fists like a warrior and yelled for his feed till his face grew red. He was soon known as Garbh, the Brawny. For some reason King David adored William particularly, though he loved young Malcolm as well and recognised him as heir. Perhaps it was a relief to the ageing King to return to the company of his grandsons after having made a slight fool of himself while siding to support his niece the Empress at Winchester, on which hazardous occasion he had nearly been killed. After that, he seemed to accept the fact that Maud herself would never reign: she had not taken the opportunity to get herself crowned and anointed while in London, and had merely asked the citizens for too much money, which angered them. Soon her son Henry, especially after Prince Eustace's death, was assumed by the English to be their next king in time, though not yet. Stephen occupied the throne till his death, and in the meantime his second son, yet another William, who was Count of Boulogne and fat like his great-grandfather the Conqueror, was married to Isabel de Warenne, only daughter and heiress of the third Earl of Warenne and Surrey, Ada's absent eldest brother William the crusader, still abroad.

Earl Henry and his Countess Ada heard with perhaps more sympathy than grief of the death of the third earl her brother at last while fighting the Saracens at Laodicea. He would undoubtedly go to heaven, which was a better place than Lewes; there, as had been the case from the beginning, his unbearable wife Ela – they called her that because there were Adelas, an Adelia and an Ada in the family already – had fought tooth and nail with the monks in the Cluniac foundation begun below the walls by the first William de Warenne and his royal wife Gundreda after their famous visit together to Burgundy and the Cluniacs. 'They had intended then to go to Rome, but were prevented by the wars between the Pope and the Emperor, and received such hospitality at Cluny that they resolved to go home and build another such, beneath the castle itself. It is probable that poor William's heart will be buried there; it is a little far to bring all of him home.'

Henry of Huntingdon remained unsmiling. He himself would have liked to ride on crusade, in obedience to the demand of fiery old Abbot Bernard from the market-place at Vézelay, where the bones of the Magdalen lay, but the church itself had been so crowded they had had to listen outside, and almost everyone of note except himself had taken the cross with the rest. King Louis of France had gone, and with him his adventurous and fascinating queen, Eleanor of Aquitaine, who faced all dangers like a man and, they said, had affairs like a man on the way; but that last thought was not charitable.

He looked at Ada, knowing he and she had done their duty to one another; there were by now five children, two of them girls, Margaret after the holy queen, and young Ada. The last baby was David, over whose cradle Countess Ada herself had been bending when he himself came in to tell her the news of the death. Ada had taken it calmly; he had never known her to be other than calm, but the remark about the crusader's body had perhaps been a little irreverent. Had it been scapegrace Ralph who died, she would no doubt have grieved more deeply. Ralph de Warenne came and went still; a knotless thread, Alice Fitzduncan called him, but he always brought them news of one kind and another from Normandy and England. Ralph had not gone on crusade either; that was some comfort to one's self-esteem.

'It will greatly vex Adelia that Reynald is not the fourth earl,' Ada said now, straightening from the cradle and smoothing her outer robe. 'The title will go instead to Fat William in his wife's right.' She smiled. 'It is a pity he and Isabel have no children as yet, but they are young still; those may come.'

The thought occurred to her, not for the first time, that perhaps William of Boulogne was too fat to beget heirs, but she realised that she had already shocked her husband slightly – it still happened at times when she forgot herself – and made the sign of the cross to please Earl Henry, saying a prayer for the dead man's soul. In fact she could hardly remember her brother Earl William at all.

'This has been a most cruel crusade,' she said. 'So many have left their bones out there to no purpose. Bernard of Clairvaux is a hard man, however holy. He was harsh to Abélard, who thought and spoke for himself, and to his own sister because she dared to marry; Abbot Bernard would not receive her when she travelled many miles to visit him. All the rest he had forced into convents, and his brothers into monasteries.' Now she had raised the ghost of Ailred; and that was a mistake. She went to her husband and put her arms around him.

'Bernard of Clairvaux has built seventy monasteries,' remarked Earl Henry reproachfully. He gave the little dry cough which troubled him now and again. 'Let us arrange a mass for your brother,' he told her, as they kissed.

She was repentant. 'If they bring the heart home, I should like, with your leave and the King's, to travel down to Lewes for the entombment. It is a long time since I saw my kin, and they will all be there, even the Beaumonts from my late mother's first marriage. Will you accompany me? You have never seen the great Cluniac monastery, and it is famous.'

'The King is ageing since my mother's death. If he should die while I was out of Scotland, there are those who would try at once to seize the power, even a supposed bastard of King Alexander's and a monk who became a bishop, then announced that he was a grandson of King Lulach and married into the family of Somerled of the Isles. Also, there are the Lady Histilla's children the Comyns, so far loyal but who knows? My father's strong rule has kept all these in their place, but I must be here, as I say.' He smiled suddenly. 'Take William

Garbh as your escort. He is too much for his nurses. Malcolm of course must not leave the country, being its next heir.'

She stroked his cheek, thinking again as she had done lately that it was worn a little; what responsibilities he had! 'I will do everything you say,' she told him softly. 'William Garbh can come and meet his Poynton cousins and fight with them on the way. It will give Malcolm a rest from fighting with him.'

'Malcolm's ambition is to become a knight,' said Malcolm's father.

By the time the third earl's heart was brought home to Lewes Ada was again pregnant, but resolved to go nevertheless and to take young Garbh with her. England was quieter now that it was generally known that young Henry Plantagenet would succeed to the throne on King Stephen's death, and the lad had been swaggering back and forth across the Channel on forays, wearing a gold broomcod in his cap to show his origins, although it was still whispered he was really Stephen's son. However he wanted Geoffrey of Anjou's broad lands as well as his mother's. He would be a power to reckon with in time, but power was better than weakness. Henry II would almost certainly pull down some of the grim unlicensed castles still rearing on their way; Ada was again glad of the escort's bright spears.

William Garbh had been taken in charge at Poynton by his cousin, yet another William de Warenne, and shown, somewhat condescendingly, the great lake where fish swam and graceful white swans floated, diving occasionally with their long necks jabbing swiftly after the fish. It seemed a pity that the swans were to be roasted for Michaelmas. He would have liked to swim in the lake, but the elder William, who had been firmly instructed not to allow him on any account to fall in, kept firm hold of his cousin's princely hand. 'Come instead and see the arms above the great door,' said William of Poynton. 'They are newly erected, and have just been painted in bright colours: come away from the water.'

He led the sturdy little boy towards the great door and they inspected the newly painted arms; on checky and azure, a lion rampant argent on gules for Mowbray and de Warenne. 'There should be a dragon,' said William of Poynton, 'for de Warenne, for it was borne at Hastings; but there was no room.'

William Garbh in any case preferred the lion; his

grandfather the King at home already used the Dragon of
Wessex, because he came of the house of Cerdic: a lion was
preferable and unusual. He himself would like to adopt one,
perhaps red on gold. He would speak about it to the King on
return, as he had already been instructed in heraldry, the new
science which made it possible for knights in the field to know
who was a friend and who an enemy. However if that had
happened his father, Earl Henry, would certainly have been
killed at the Battle of the Standard instead of riding back safely
among the enemy English knights. Nevertheless, he himself
would remember about the lion.

'Well, have you stared enough?' asked William of Poynton
with some impatience; he wanted his dinner, and it promised to
be a good one as the visitors from Scotland were of such
influence. He took young William's hand again and led him
inside the house, still smelling as it did of new plaster as well as
roasting meat. Not many had stone houses; Poynton was
already something to be remarked upon, and could not have
been built in the south, where there was still wanton destruction
of the wooden dwellings there by fire. The guests were
nevertheless journeying that way tomorrow, after resting
overnight: and one's parents would accompany them.

Lewes was reached safely by the travellers at last, and William
Garbh saw the great rearing castle built by his ancestor the first
William de Warenne, who had fought at Hastings with his
dragon shield; and clustering below, the famous Cluniac
monastery with its outbuildings for healing the sick, its
herbarium and its chapel, where the crusader's heart of the
third earl was to be buried with all the dead de Warennes and
their wives and heirs since the Conqueror's time, last century.

He was led in, holding his mother's hand, to where before
the high altar the bones of the first earl lay entombed with
those of his wife the Lady Gundreda, joint founders as they had
been of the Cluniac monastery dedicated to St. Pancras.
Chanting sounded already from the choir; the white-robed
Abbot bent over William's mother's hand and gave her his
blessing. There were other relations here as well as the Poynton
couple, who had come with them, and uncle Ralph who was
always to be found everywhere by some means. William's
mother went to kiss her sister Gundred, married by now to yet a
third husband from Kendal; also the widow of the dead
crusader, Countess Ela, who did not seem to be in any notable

grief though she wore weeds as was proper. A knight, evidently
the Earl of Salisbury, was in close attendance on her. Her
young daughter Isabel, heiress to the title, accompanied by her
fat amiable husband William of Boulogne and his sister Mary,
was present, and showed the devilish attractiveness of her
mother's de Bellesme blood as well as the fine bones of the
Vermandois; young as he was, William Garbh knew it would be
difficult to forget Isabel de Warenne; she was like a princess of
romance. Reynald his uncle and the latter's wife Adelia, no
longer chattering while in church, followed with several
step-relations, the de Beaumonts, formerly powerful adherents
of King Stephen and before that advisers to old King Henry,
and still owning broad lands in Normandy at Meulan and
elsewhere besides the Honour of Leicester itself. Some of this
William knew then, and the rest he learned afterwards.
Meantime they all took their places and the crusader's heart, in
its precious casket, was solemnly borne in to much chanting,
censed and then entombed: the clouds of incense rose
fragrantly and ascended among the new stone pillars between
the adjoining graves.

Ada meantime felt the child in her womb give a leap. It had
already begun to do so on the journey down, but she knew, this
being her sixth pregnancy, that that need mean nothing
imminent. There was time, after Mass had been said, to show
William Garbh his grandparents' tombs, especially that of her
own mother, Isabel de Vermandois, hardly remembered as she
had died when Ada was so young. The effigy lay elegantly in its
folded robes and wimple, and the carved features gave away
nothing; but this woman had not been happy in her second
marriage to a man who had forever loved a queen, the wife of
another.

Ada spoke suddenly to her son, in a low voice. 'That is your
grandfather the second earl's tomb beside hers,' she said. 'He
used to mock old King Henry in their youth together, when the
King was a penniless prince without enough money for a horse
to follow the hunt. My father used to call him Deerfoot because
he had to run after the rest. The King never forgave him, I
believe: and in the end married the woman my father loved.'

She lit a candle for the souls of her father and mother, and
then paused briefly at the tomb of old William, first earl, and
his wife Gundreda. Through Gundreda came royal blood: she
had died in childbirth, and it was not till afterwards, in Rufus's
reign, that the old warrior, her widower, had been granted the

Surrey earldom. Nevertheless he had got himself three
hundred manors after Hastings, being a favourite of the new
King his father-in-law. They said the first William de Warenne
had been very tall, a giant of a man.

Countess Ela had meantime marched out, skirts trailing, on
the arm of Salisbury who was evidently her next destined prey.
Ada followed with Garbh up the ascent to the castle, wondering
after all if her labour were perhaps starting earlier than
expected; it was possible, with the lurching there had been on
the journey. That meant enduring Ela's hospitality, but not for
longer than the lying-in should take. If this proved a girl, she
had already decided to call her Matilda, after the Conqueror's
queen and Stephen's, also King David's dead wife; that would
please the old King greatly.

'My aunt of Surrey,' remarked Garbh then, 'seems in a bad
humour.' His round little face looked up at his mother, all of a
grin. He was, at the same time, proud of her in the dignified
robes and narrow gold circlet she wore, showing that she was a
princess of Scotland and would soon be its queen. That would,
of course, be after grandfather died; and one did not want that
to happen yet.

'She comes of a bad-tempered family,' remarked Ada, not
loudly; the pains were increasing.

'So do we, on your side.'

'Come,' Ada said, and paused to have a last look at her parents'
tombs. Perhaps they were closer now, husband and wife, in
death; death no doubt made one understand many things. The
colours were still bright on the effigies, as they had been above
the door at Poynton. Behind them, the crusader's heart was left
alone in the silent church, entombed in its casket.

During Ada's labour good Fat William, by now fourth earl, with
his young wife and sister and their party, offered to take
William Garbh to see the new cathedral at Chichester, built
when the former one at Selsey had threatened to slide into the
sea. The child rode off happily on someone's crupper, and
returned to find a new baby sister, but although pleased
enough with her, noted that she had no hair or fingernails.

'That is because she arrived a little early,' said Ada from the
bed. 'The hair and nails will grow.'

'I hope so. We saw carved stone panels at Chichester, very
old. One was of Christ in the house of Mary and Martha, and
the other was of the raising of Lazarus. Mary of Boulogne said

a prayer. She wants to be a nun.'

'You must tell that to Malcolm when you return.'

'I can tell Malcolm anything. I can throw Malcolm on the floor. I am bigger than he is.'

Ada begged Countess Ela to take him away and somehow occupy him; she was still tired, and news of the safe birth must be sent to Scotland. Afterwards, she hoped Ela would not have frightened the child with fearsome stories as was her unpleasant habit, having made her own daughter Isabel constantly fearful in childhood: but nothing could really frighten William Garbh.

In fact, William himself was regaled with stories he had mostly heard already, about the fairy Melusine disappearing through the church window and Black Fulk of Anjou's Countess – he himself was said to be descended from the devil – being burnt alive by him in her wedding dress. There was a new one, however, about Black Fulk's son, Geoffrey Greygown, being forced by his father to wear a saddle and bridle and crawl about on all fours, which seemed a pointless pursuit in any circumstances. Garbh was more interested in watching Countess Ela's discontented and bitter face; perhaps it was because she was a widow. Isabel herself and Fat William, both of whom had been kind to him at Chichester, had gone off now somewhere; he could hear their laughter, and pricked his ears. Countess Ela raised her head in its widow's veil spitefully.

'They may laugh now, but *he* will never give her children.'

William Garbh listened courteously, and thought again of his mother in the great bed with the new baby which lacked its fingernails. He mentioned that there were always children in his own family, in Scotland. The bitter face grew white with envy; Countess Ela's eyes glistened like those of a wary animal.

'Now, maybe, but never later. There is the curse on you all; the Atheling line will not last. Your grandsire has built abbey after abbey, but it will avail him nothing.'

William Garbh crossed himself, as he had been taught to do when disturbed; it banished the devil. Whether for this reason or not, Countess Ela sent for her women then to take him away; and after he had gone she sat picking discontentedly at her embroidery. How slow the time was to pass! Soon now, one hoped, Earl Patrick of Salisbury would come riding with the Pope's permission, and she would then become his wife. It was swift to follow, no doubt, after the late earl's funeral, or rather that of his returned heart; but every woman was entitled to solace in her bed, and it was some years now since the third earl had ridden off on crusade. She herself, unlike the de Warennes, would refuse to be buried at last in the detested monastery below the walls; there had been constant squabbling with the Abbot over tithes since William her husband left for the Holy Land.

Ada noticed that William Garbh was quieter on the journey back than he had been, but took it that the solemnity of the occasion at Lewes had impressed him. As children will, he said nothing, merely staring with interest at the baby Matilda, who lost her wrinkled look on the way and by the time they neared Carlisle, had begun to grow some hair. There was unlikely, his mother thought, to be anything the matter with Garbh; no doubt he was beginning to miss the company of his brother Malcolm and the fights they by custom had, rolling over and over together on the floor-straw.

'Soon now we will be home,' she told Garbh, smiling. How pleasant it was to think of that, and how different from her own earlier journey up here to be married, then knowing nobody at all! Now, her very marriage had helped put an end to the differences between north and south, a little; even here, where in a cleft hidden valley the Saxons had held out against the Norman invasion well into the reign of Rufus. They had, perhaps, suspected her own Norman blood hereabouts at first, but her cheerful easy ways among them, and the fact that she had borne healthy children to their prince, whom they thought of as part Saxon and part Gael, forgetting his father's upbringing at King Henry's court, had reassured them, and a welcome awaited her along the roads. She opened the curtains of the litter wide, to show them not only William Garbh but the new baby. Soon, again, the frowning mountains gave way to the low plains by the firth; and Earl Henry himself, accompanied by his friend the Comyn, Histilla's husband, who was never far from his side, rode out with a concourse to meet her, pennants waving like the oriflamme of St. Denis that had commenced the fatal crusade: and kissed his new daughter tenderly, also his wife.

Five

Ada was happy. In many ways – and she was to know it more
fully later – this day was the crown of her life. At least in part, it
was due to her description of the glories of the Cluniac priory
at Lewes that had caused her husband Earl Henry, and the
King his father, to build a Cistercian one of the new modified
order, almost as glorious though more remote, here within
sight of the Solway flats with a view across the water to
Galloway. In the bitter January wind all the nobility of the land
had ridden in for the consecration; Uchtred of Galloway, the
hostage himself, who had donated money in gift to the new
abbey; the rival heirs for the kingdom, Histilla and her husband
Richard Comyn; Ada's own friend Alice Fitzduncan and her
husband and son William and two daughters; de Morville, the
Constable of Scotland; the one Gael the King kept about him,
Earl Gillemichael of Fife; the people of Cumbria, showing that
the King of Scots was their accepted prince. Across the narrow
water old Fergus, Lord of Galloway, was said to be ill; his
younger son Gilbert had not come today. Otherwise, after this
ceremony was over, they would all keep the King's Yule
together in Carlisle.

The white-robed monks chanted as they had done in the
south, processing down between the carved white pillars.
Holme Cultram would be a source of culture, healing and
knowledge to all generations, preserving as it would the new,
strict learning of Abbot Bernard and its provisions with which
oneself, privately, could not altogether agree; if men and
women were to prefer virginity to marriage, what would
become of the human race in general, and kings in particular?
There must, however, be nothing said of that; it was a delicate
matter. She herself knelt here today beside Earl Henry, father
of her children, surely soon now to become King of Scots.
Their four eldest were here, young David and chubby Matilda
having been thought too young for the long ceremony and

being, accordingly, left behind with their nurses and a hound puppy to entertain them at the castle. But the two boys on the Earl's side, Malcolm with his almost girlish beauty, William Garbh with his strength, made Ada proud; and the loveliness of Margaret, her eldest girl, kneeling close by, was said to resemble that of her namesake and great-grandmother Margaret Atheling herself. Young Ada was less notable, and placid, like her mother. They would make good marriages, possibly abroad; with the increasing stability of the kingdom it was possible to think of alliances of the kind, but there was time yet. Old King David, his snowy beard shining in the light of the many candles, knelt above them and a little apart, an anointed king. Soon it would be Henry's turn for that. Ada turned her head a little to look at her husband, deep in his prayers. Their love and affection had increased with the years; it had been a happy marriage. Earl Henry would make as good and able a king as he had a husband and father.

She lowered her eyes from staring at King David; the thought strayed through her mind that King Edward the Confessor, the model on whom all of the Atheling princes had been encouraged to base their conduct, had been said all his life to have white hair. One wondered why his Norman mother Emma had so disliked him, preferring the drunken son of her second marriage to Cnut. All that was however long ago.

The consecration of the great abbey proceeded, with the new Bishop Christian of Galloway – old John of Glasgow, the King's friend who should have been here, had lately died – marking each cross on each pillar with holy oil, again in the sign of the cross from left to right round the church. Soon the little flame above the sanctuary burned bright in its red lamp; and with the coming early dark, all the jewel-colours of the great glass windows were meantime extinguished. How pleasant it was to think that this abbey would remain, as a memorial to herself and Earl Henry and his father, after all of them were dead! She and her husband would not, however, be buried here; that would no doubt happen at Kelso, which King David had made to be of great importance since transferring the monks there lately from Selkirk. He would be remembered for his building of great abbeys if for nothing else. Founders, like old William de Warenne and Gundreda in the south, with masses sung daily for their souls' weal; one need not fear death. Why think of it? Ada the Countess made her mind turn away, and listened to the chanting.

For some reason her mind, ever thinking of things to be done, ranged then to Northumbria, across country. Since its devastation by the Conqueror and, later, his son Robert Curthose, the place was a desert except for its busy port. Not a soul at the time of the invasion last century had been left alive among the burned houses, the ravaged lands. All that had still to be mended, healed, restored; and her husband's title of earl of the province must be made to mean something, to promise better things. There was still unrest since Curthose's building long since of his fort of Newcastle, and one hoped that his kinsman young Henry Plantagenet, knighted only last year by King David here in Carlisle, would bring his strong neglected hands to bear in a friend's grip when he inherited England. He had promised, in exchange for the desired knighting, to honour the Scots title in Northumbria and here. 'He enjoyed much hospitality from my father-in-law in youth,' Ada reminded herself. At present, it was uncertain what was happening in England, and news filtered from there with more difficulty than ever since King Stephen's slow illness and the death of his queen. Even Ralph had not ridden up for over a year.

The long ceremony came to an end. Ada the Countess rose at last from her knees, and, followed by her sons and daughters, emerged with one hand borne high on the King's, the other on her husband's. Outside, the commons jostled, each one in the crowd hoping for a clear sight of the royal party, and the King, as he always did, listened to pleas in person. David of Scotland did not at any time spare himself; he was to ride north to Moray in the summer, to found yet another new abbey at Kinloss; then down to Dryburgh, in company with his friend Hugh de Morville the Constable. She and Earl Henry would however remain in Carlisle; it was not yet time to have to consider affairs beyond the gleaming Solway and the Firth, but Ada was herself considering the founding of a town at a place named Haddington, in Lothian.

The escort surrounded them at last, and they rode back to Carlisle by the light of torches, flaring orange in the dark and the winter wind.

'And so I have ridden across the breadth of Scotland, my sister, having come up at first by sea for greater safety, and expecting to find you still in Carlisle.'

'This place is better in summer, and the children can play by the river.' They were near the broad-running Teviot: but only the youngest girl was with her.

'Well, at any event I have brought your gifts safely, strapped to the saddle at last.'

Ralph de Warenne, bachelor still, stretched his legs agreeably now they were freed from their greaves, left Ada to open the aforementioned gifts, and went to the castle window. The King's town of Roxburgh was different from the wild land he had passed through only yesterday; the great Forest of Selkirk, with, unexpectedly, a high narrow waterfall, and near it the strange sight of Culdee monks still, with their shaven foreheads, lurking in abandoned places. They had given him and his following shelter for the night, in the tumbledown monastery King David no longer recognised since building his great Kelso foundation. This country, however, was safer far than England, where one might still be attacked even on the good Roman roads; King Stephen was dying in Westminster, and the young Henry Plantagenet waited to cross to claim his crown at last, having taken to himself, meantime, a rich and well-dowered bride.

Ralph spoke of the bride to Ada while she unfolded what he had brought her, and gasped at its exotic beauty; it was a length of brocade of the East, which Eleanor of Aquitaine had herself made fashionable since the crusade on which she had journeyed with her recently divorced husband, King Louis VII of France. Ada held the bright shimmering stuff up against herself, laughing a little: she knew she no longer had the figure she had once had as a girl, after bearing six children. She laid the rich brocade carefully over a folding chair in order not to spoil it; the straw on the floor was changed often, but still could not compete with Eleanor's likewise introduced carpets, first seen maybe in Saladin's silken tent. Most folk here, unable to bear the thought of having those on the floor if they had them at all, hung them on the wall or else over tables. The Syrians, one understood, prayed on them.

'It is most beautiful,' she said now of the brocade, and went to kiss Ralph in gratitude, rubbing his rough cheek against hers affectionately; it was a long time since their days together in Bellencombre. 'Tell me of Duchess Eleanor; you have seen her?'

'I saw her at Rouen, with the Empress, who has governed Normandy on her son's behalf better than she would have done England. Eleanor herself is remarkable. She is eleven years

older than her bridegroom, and they say King Louis was
secretly loth to lose her and her lands, but there were only two
daughters after fourteen years of marriage; however, they say
Henry has done better by her already.' He winked in the old
way.

Ada was thoughtful. 'They say also that she even caused the
crusade to be lost by dallying too long with her women in a
valley full of fountains. King Louis had to divert his troops to
defend the valley, and in the end to save himself at last by
climbing a tree.'

'Well, he has got himself a new wife, who will maybe cause
him to stay on the ground. I saw Ela at Lewes.' He grimaced.
Ada asked with courtesy after her sister-in-law, and Ralph
shrugged.

'Oh, she is content enough with Salisbury since they were
wed. Isabel still has no sign of any child by Fat William.'

'What a gossip you are.' She poured him wine and took some
herself. 'I have heard nothing from there for two years,' she
said. 'Maybe by the end Reynald will be earl, after all.'

'Who knows?' Ralph picked up his young niece Matilda, who
had come running in free of the nurses: the other children
were, meantime, with their grandfather in Edinburgh, for old
King David doted on their company, especially that of Garbh.
Matilda chuckled, and held out her hands towards the spread
brocade; it shone, she decided, like a field of flowers.

'Smell,' said Ralph. 'It was packed in sandalwood from where
the caravans come.' He let the little girl lean her plump face
against the brocade. An aromatic scent rose with the warmth,
bringing a far world into the solar. 'Everything is changing,'
said Ada. 'Up here, we are ignorant of much, except for the
merchants who come from Berwick with foreign wares.'

'Your mother,' said Ralph to Matilda, 'will make herself a
grand robe and line it with fur against the cold, and maybe
there will be enough left to make a coat for you also.'

'Coat,' said Matilda. She fingered her uncle's surcoat
reflectively. She was not as strong as the other children, except
Malcolm who was also delicate, and like him took fevers easily;
it was no doubt due to her premature birth. It was hot today in
the valley, with a clinging unusual heat that brought flies,
unlike snell Scotland at any time. The child slid off Ralph's
knee and went to examine the brocade more closely. Ada took
her daughter's hand firmly.

'You must not touch,' she said, and turning to Ralph, 'Tell

me more of Duchess Eleanor. They say she writes songs in her own language.'

'Well, you know as much as I; she has been little seen since the marriage. I doubt if young Henry will be faithful; he grasps what he may, and Eleanor's broad lands in the south of France mean as much to him as her body, no doubt. He attracts women, however, though he is less handsome than his father, who died over young.'

'He is careless of his appearance, certainly, but has charm. He will make a strong king when it comes about, though the divorce caused scandal even here. The English would never accept his mother, but they are sick of wars and a weak king; no doubt they will welcome Henry and his Eleanor when they come to Westminster to be crowned.'

She thought of poor King Stephen, and his heir Eustace dead; Henry had been preferred to Fat William, the second son who was now Count of Boulogne. She remembered Stephen's kindness and that of his queen at Westminster long ago, and of how she owed her own marriage to Queen Matilda. 'It is strange to think that not many years back, he invaded here, and the King and my husband fought against him, and won or lost as fortune wavered,' she said. 'How useless wars are! In the end, they prove nothing.'

'Well, Stephen chose to come over and get himself crowned in despite of old King Henry's daughter and her right. I doubt it proved a crown of thorns.'

'Well, he will soon die.'

She thought again of how secure and happy they were here in the north, free of dying kings, warring barons and unsafe ways. It had been safer for Ralph to ride across the wild inland valleys than to take a straight road in the south. Please God, Ada thought, when my husband is king matters will continue so.

She fingered the rich brocade, thinking once more of Eleanor of Aquitaine, shortly to be Queen of England. Perhaps one day they would meet.

Within a day, little Matilda was tossing with fever. Earl Henry, returned from Kelso where he had been discussing matters with the bursar, the early foundation by his father having been put in his charge, as Dryburgh had in de Morville's, bent now over his sick daughter's bed and kissed her; he loved all of his children. 'It is the heat,' he told Ada. 'How hot it was riding! She will sweat soon, and be rid of it.'

But it was Earl Henry himself who sweated, within a night and a day, and grievously. He took to his bed and could neither eat, drink, nor presently know anyone. He raved in delirium, and shortly, to Ada's horror, began to emit blood from the nose and mouth. Was it the new smallpox brought from the East, for which they said one hung scarlet curtains to rival the vesicles, driving out their power? There had been no time to do so, or even to send for a priest.

Suddenly Earl Henry spoke clearly, the sweat still in great beads on his forehead. 'It is the malign sickness,' he said. 'I know that I will die. Have prayers said; do not go near the children yet.' Then he lapsed back into disjointed murmurings, and his head fell forward on his chest. Henry of Huntingdon, heir to Scotland and Scotland's hope, was dead. It had happened too swiftly for her to credit it. Dazed, she sent for a priest to come. Then she heard herself, as if she had been some other woman, give orders that the damned brocade should be burnt, for it had brought the Eastern sickness with it. The child Matilda was dead also: Ada hardly remembered to mourn for her last child's life. The charm that brought ill to all her house, the charm of the old blind king, had killed Earl Henry, 'him whom I have loved beyond all mortals.' Those could be Ailred's words: and also her own.

Henry of Huntingdon's body was buried at Kelso. There was no leisure, in the summer's heat, for a great funeral procession throughout the land. In every church he and his father had raised, masses were sung, crowds gathered and women wept for the brave and beautiful prince, who should have ruled over them, 'the pride of youth, the joy of knights, the glory of old men.' In his monastery, Ailred of Rievaulx shed tears like a woman. Grief was felt everywhere for the aged King, for the widowed Countess, for the eleven-year-old child who would inherit the throne; *woe to the land whose king is a child*! Yesterday they had been secure in hope; today, all was quicksand. The death of Earl Henry would surely kill his father with grief.

But King David lived eleven months. Before he died, he sent for Ada to make provision for the new young heir; Malcolm must be sent on progress through the land, accompanied by six earls; the people must see their future king. As for Garbh, the old man took him to Newcastle and showed him to the people there, telling them that this was to be their ruler in Northumbria. Garbh, still full of bewildered sadness for his father, was proud of his new importance; and Ada the widowed Countess, when she could do so, rode to Edinburgh, leaving Earl Henry's body and their daughter's in the new tomb at Kelso surrounded by lighted candles. She was not to join them there for twenty-six years.

Six

'It was the will of God.'

Instead of lying on a bed of sickness, age and grief, David of Scotland greeted his widowed daughter-in-law shod, robed and crowned, seated with his lords behind him and his sword resting across his knees. At his feet sat William Garbh, arrayed in a new mourning-tunic made to allow for his growth. He was already taller and broader by far than when, only a short time ago, his mother had last seen him. Malcolm was elsewhere.

William, evidently instructed, rose, bowed to the King, and came to escort his mother to where David sat on his great folding chair. They approached together and knelt: on the way Ada noted that Gillemichael, Earl of Fife, the only born Gael the King would usually suffer to have about him, was absent, no doubt with Malcolm on his progress through the kingdom. That had been arranged at once.

The old King received her lips on his hand, then spoke. Nearer him, one could see that sorrow had wasted his face till it seemed all eyes above the full white beard and below the crown's rim. He was in fact by now like old Merlin, whose ancient prophesies were at that moment being repeated everywhere in England. The double eagle Merlin had foreseen had come: Eleanor of Aquitaine, Queen of France and shortly to become Queen of England, near now in space and time. Her brocade that carried death in its folds had come already to Scotland, but no doubt she had known and intended nothing of that.

'I have sent Prince Malcolm, heir to this kingdom of Scotia, on progress with six of the seven earls, Fife at their head,' the King said in a clear voice. 'It is needful that the commons of this land know who is to be their next king, and to see him for themselves. They will love him meantime for his beauty, and later for his strength.'

William Garbh grinned, unable to help himself, and his grandfather ruffled his hair. 'Ay, lad, ay: but there is the Gael

54

and the Scot of Lothian, and the Norsemen and the men of the
Isles, and my Welsh in Cumbria, and the Picts of Galloway, to
be welded together in one. I have made Scotland a kingdom in
my lifetime, not without battle here and there: but a king who is
a child needs wise counsel. That he will get from you, my
daughter, wife to my dear son who I had hoped would reign
after me.' The voice trembled for the first time. 'My lords here
also I can trust,' King David said then. 'They have sworn to
honour the fourth Malcolm as they would have honoured the
third, my father.'

The deep eyes looked at Ada from beneath the gold of the
crown. 'Have no fear,' the King said. 'The Prince's escort is well
armed. It will take him north into Moray and Ross and the
western parts, and he will be well beseen in all of them.'

She saw the wisdom of it, though she continued anxious for
Malcolm till he should return; he was after all only eleven years
old. Before they all went in together to the high table the King
beckoned to Garbh again, making the boy kneel. He then
created him Earl of Northampton, a title of great importance in
England.

'That is the honour I hold from my late wife,' David said.
'You will hold it in trust and defend it well.'

William Garbh received the honour, seeming already less of a
child. Ada was aware of the old King's astuteness: he had
wasted no time in ensuring that the English title was conveyed
before the arrival of the new King Henry might make its
disposal uncertain. As for Garbh, he was pleased enough to be
an earl at nine years old.

Malcolm returned safely at last, having impressed everyone by
his beauty as the King had foreseen; but he had already become
a little boastful. All who had met with him at the places where
they had rested, mostly his grandfather's abbeys, had made
much of him, and the folk on the roads had called out blessings
and had brought him gifts of carved wood and narwhal horn
and the like. He was also impressed with himself for having
been as far north as Moray, which province remembered the
good King MacBeth and was as a rule hostile to the line of
Ceann Mór. 'There is a tale being told up there I had not heard
in the south, although the man is held prisoner still at
Roxburgh,' he told William Garbh later, when they were alone.

The tale concerned the monk named Wimond who after ten
years had by popular demand become a bishop, as he was tall

and handsome. He had then declared himself to be the grandson of King Lulach, MacBeth's stepson who had reigned as briefly in his time as the second Duncan. Wimond had then taken the name of Malcolm MacHeth, Heth having no doubt been the man who had married Lulach's daughter. It was the old Tanist inheritance raising its head, but less well proven than Histilla's right, let alone that of Fitzduncan. MacHeth had then consolidated his position by marrying a daughter of Somerled of the Isles. 'He has sons and daughters,' said Malcolm. 'In the end our grandfather imprisoned him after a fight. I have never seen him at Roxburgh when we were there: they must keep him close.'

William Garbh agreed that he had never seen the former bishop either. 'He says that he is rightful King of Scots,' said Malcolm, surveying himself briefly in the burnished metal mirror and combing his beautiful long fair curling locks with his fingers. They had called him in the north – he would never tell William of it – Malcolm the Maiden because of his bright complexion. He had already moreover decided to become the Knight Galahad described in the gestes of Arthur, and, like him, to remain a virgin. It was fashionable to do so now that Cistercian thought was everywhere, and Malcolm's tutors had told him of it. Also, he was an Atheling, and they preferred to imitate King Edward the Confessor, who had however been married but had ignored his queen. As for King Lulach, he had been known to everyone in the brief course of events as Lulach the Fool; and it was easy to pretend to be a dead fool's grandson. He himself, Malcolm IV of Scots, would fight any pretenders of the kind; Galahad, like his father Lancelot, had also fought bravely.

William Garbh brought his elder brother down to earth. 'There was another who called himself Malcolm and said he was a bastard of King Alexander's,' he remarked now. 'Our grandfather says that was unlikely, but he fought that Malcolm also.'

The present Malcolm reflected that even William Fitzduncan had several bastards besides his one legitimate son, the Boy of Egremont. He then made a statement that could have come from a much older head and probably had. 'Henry FitzEmpress, who will certainly keep the English throne, our grandfather says has one dream: to renew the borders of England exactly as they were in the time of his own grandsire, old King Henry Beauclerc the Conqueror's son, who married our great-aunt the Good Queen. If he tries to annex Northumbria, you must make war.'

'Then you must aid me,' replied Willilam Garbh with spirit. 'It is not like the days when King Edgar on his deathbed divided the kingdom into two, the north part to his brother King Alexander and the south part to our grandfather, the youngest brother, who was an earl then. It is all one now, and we must fight together.'

'Well, that remains to be seen,' said Malcolm the Maiden loftily, and continued to comb his hair. He had been taught in the north to be proud of it. William's appearance was nothing compared to his own. William need not in any case think that his earldom made him as important as oneself, the future king.

King David spent the months which remained to him in instructing Ada in her duties as guardian and, virtually, ruler of Scotland till her son Malcolm should become of age. 'A woman, my own niece the Empress, was not acceptable to the English, being a stranger, but you are known among us,' he told her. 'Nor will you lack advice if you should need it, or a strong arm by way of my lords. They and the bishops know well enough that it is best to have a central rule rather than separate factions such as there have been in the past. My brother Edgar was mistaken in splitting the kingdom into two parts, north and south, when he was dying; had Alexander's wife had sons, there would be trouble now. As it is, there is stirring already among the Northmen, who think that because I am old I am helpless.' He smiled grimly. 'That is not so, as they will find while I live. There has arisen also this Somerled, whoever his father may have been, in the Isles themselves, the Sudreys; and the one also further south who calls himself King of Man. All these may rise up at my death, likewise the men of Galloway.'

She recalled Uchtred, loyal enough, who had gone home; but his brother Gilbert was causing disturbances in those parts. The King was still speaking, lying by now as he did on the bed where he would soon die.

'My father Malcolm Ceann Mór and I have welded the kingdom together as one in our different times, and thus it should stay. As soon as I am dead, have your son anointed on the sacred stone of Scone, and guarded thereafter. Do not bury me in Scone, beside my late dear wife: I had hoped that our bones would mingle, but at the time I buried her there I thought my son would reign after me.' There were tears in his eyes. 'As it is, the ceremony at Scone must be undertaken too quickly for a further burial there; bury me instead in Dunfermline, beside my parents, then go straight to the anointing of your son.' He lay silent for instants, as though he prayed. 'You are a strong woman and a wise,' he told her. 'My son Henry was fortunate in his wife. Guard my kingdom well; guard Scotland until its king is grown strong.'

'I will.' It was like the vow she had made at her marriage, when she and Earl Henry had exchanged rings. This was a sacred trust, and she would keep it. It occurred to her already that besides the anointing, she would make them crown Malcolm during the ceremony, as it was done in England but hitherto not here. There would be no doubt then among them who was King.

David of Scotland asked presently for a priest to be sent for, as he knew he would shortly die.

Ada had sent for the priest. Meantime she knelt at the King's left hand, while the boy Malcolm knelt at his right. William Garbh was at the bed's foot, and it was on him, strangely, that the dying man's eyes rested. The failing voice told them that as soon as he himself was dead, Gillemichael of Fife must take the ring from his finger and place it on Malcolm's own. 'Then you will be a king like my father and myself. Before the priests come and I shrive my soul, I will say a poem to you about my father Malcolm Ceann Mór. This was written despite the English chroniclers, who say of him that he was a destroyer and nothing else.'

He then said the poem, which old Donald Bán had repeated long ago, about the greatest king to reign in Alban. 'Do not,' David said at the end, 'render homage to England for any but the English fiefs. Remember it. Scotland is a separate kingdom, owing no allegiance to them; I say it who was myself brought up in the English court and know their ways. Remember.'

The great gentle eyes were fading: none present were old enough to remember Margaret Atheling or to know that they resembled hers. It was sixty years since her death and her husband's. David himself, their youngest son, was seventy-three years old. The priest had already come, with the viaticum: Ada rose, and signalled that everyone should leave the death-chamber. She kissed the King's hand on leaving: after he had confessed what sins he had, it would not be allowed to anyone to have speech with him again: he must go straight to God.

She made herself, at once and without delay, prepare for the anointing at Scone of Malcolm IV, also his crowning. It was after that that they brought her word that King David was dead, and she arranged the burial.

The long obsequies took place, after the Scone ceremony had been made ready; there was the familiar chanting of monks in black or white, the presence of mitred bishops, the censing of the bier itself, the bearing away of the remains of the last son of Malcolm III and Margaret Atheling, who had brought the new ways to Scotland and had not been greatly liked by some; and Ada's own sons, even young David, taking part in the long train behind it. There were the seven earls, Fife, Atholl, Mar, Strathearn, Buchan, Angus, Menteith, with their followings; the silent folk lining the ways as they all passed by; there was much mourning for the good King, the last son of Malcolm the Great Chief, who had given five kings to Scotland. She herself would never now be queen; she was however Earl Henry's widow, and proud; also, the guardian of all the land from Ross to Northumbria.

Word had already come that the Northmen were plundering Aberdeen. She must send enough men there at once to ensure that the raid was not repeated, that a boy on the throne did not mean weakness to be exploited. Young Malcolm was duly set on the sacred stone; how plain it was, and said to have been Jacob's pillow at Bethel, hallowed by every king of Scots since the beginning, never to be lost or taken away! She must guard all such things: and having seen Malcolm's fair hair surmounted by a crown in the late May sunlight, had the less time to be a mother to her children thereafter. Young Ada would take her place meantime: there were already strong adverse stirrings in Galloway. Ada the Countess sent men there also, preserving her own calm.

She found time for a great parchment to be written out at Kelso, with an illuminated capital showing both the old and the young kings. David was shown as he had been before his hair and beard turned white, holding his sceptre and orb. Young Malcolm, smooth-faced and with his long hair combed beneath the crown, held the sceptre and, instead, a sword: they could take note of that. In addition, Ada had ordered a secret device of her own, of de Warenne; the twisted dragon of the long ships, which three centuries ago had borne her own fierce ancestors by sea to Normandy and which the first William de Warenne had borne on his shield at Hastings. Those of future generations might ponder over the capital and understand, or else not, as they chose. Meantime the charter should lie safe enough in the chest at Kelso, the great abbey where Earl Henry himself lay buried.

Ada firmed her lips beneath the widow's veil forever now shading her forehead. She would read each document carefully before setting her signature to it, remembering the Latin she had been taught at Bellencombre. The signature would be clear, to be remembered and respected: that of the King's mother, Ada the Countess.

PART II

One

'You are a fool as well as a traitor, my liege. Because William the Boy of Egremont drowned by accident in the Strid at Bolton last year, you think no one will supplant you now whatever you do. Henry Plantagenet has broken the oath he swore to our grandfather when King David knighted him, at his own request, at Carlisle eighteen years ago, when Henry swore then to honour the Scots possession of the very lands he has taken from you now – and will not even grant you knighthood in exchange. What sort of a figure do you cut, you, the King? It is as great an insult as William Rufus cast at our great-grandsire King Malcolm Canmore when he rode down to Gloucester, an old man, to make peace when William was ill, and by the time he got there William was recovered and would not receive him, having asked him earlier to come on so long a journey in his old age. They have always treated us as dependants when they can, and you have allowed it to happen once again. Huntingdon was ours by right of our grandfather's marriage, and the lands beyond Tweed ours also, needing no homage to England.'

William Garbh had lost his habitual high colour and was white with rage. Malcolm the Maiden, on the other hand, elegantly clad as was his custom, had crimsoned all over his girlish face. He loathed having been made to look a fool, especially by Henry Plantagenet: he loved splendour and power, and had admired the second Henry for his grasp of both, looking forward to being made a knight by the only person in the islands who could so dub him; and the Plantagenet had refused, smiling and giving no reason after he, Malcolm, had ceded the lands asked for and knelt to the English King at Chester. Malcolm was near tears, which he would never willingly shed in his brother's presence; he had enjoyed the company of the King of England, so different from himself, heedless of what he wore, dressed always in a short cape like some poor man and caring nothing, and neglecting his hands like any groom. Henry had however exerted his full charm until it became evident that what he had required of the young King of Scots was the overlordship of the three northern counties as it had been in the time of his grandfather, Henry I, known by now as Beauclerc for his even script. The continued Honour of Huntingdon had been thrown at Malcolm as a sop: and Huntingdon meant continued relations with the English Court, elegant though strict nowadays, and the improved laws and conditions in England since the late King Stephen's unlicensed castles had been razed and their owners made to obey a strong hand at last. There could be no advancement lacking England's friendship. Malcolm tried to retrieve his dignity despite still not having become, at seventeen, a knight as was his heart's desire.

'Remember that I am your King,' he said stiffly. 'To call me traitor and fool is to make one of yourself.' He added, mumbling slightly and spoiling the late effect, that Huntingdon had in any case by now lapsed to England as a result of the death of their grandmother's son by her first marriage. William Garbh made a vulgar noise, dismissing the information.

'Huntingdon is ours, and always should be. What alarms Henry is the arrangement you have made, or rather our mother has, to marry our two elder sisters abroad, to Holland and Brittany, in a year or two; he fears it will give Scotland too many allies overseas. That is why he has humbled you.'

Malcolm did not reply, and instead stalked out, the budge lining of his robe flapping behind him with imitative anger. Since taking the reins of government from the steady hands of their mother he had in fact fallen out with many of the great lords; this latest intelligence would not placate them. To lose the easy access to the sea Northumbria offered was a deprivation to Scotland's trade, beginning formerly to thrive again after the old Conqueror's devastation of that province. William Garbh, left alone, strode up and down in impotent fury. The English to possess Northumbria, of which he himself, at nine years old, had been made lord by his grandfather King David, with all present swearing loyalty! It was an insult, as he had told his brother; the devil take to hell his own descendant Henry of Anjou, and Henry's old grandfather as well; Beauclerc the Conqueror's youngest son had made a poor enough husband to one's great-aunt the Good Queen, with twenty bastards of his own to support and marry.

However Garbh knew he would make it up with Malcolm:

they always did. Both brothers were aware that they differed from one another in all possible ways except high temper, and must endure the fact and try to control it. Their mother had impressed this on them often, and Countess Ada had their respect. She had handled like a man, in her time of governance, the revolt of the so-called Malcolm MacHeth's sons, helped by their uncle Somerled, who now said he himself was a descendant of Con of the Hundred Battles. That revolt had been in the very year of Malcolm's accession; and Somerled was still at large in the Isles. Malcolm still, his brother knew, needed support; he was vainglorious, and not to have received the coveted knighthood after all from Henry II must have been a bitter disappointment. The devil's descendant of Anjou evidently possessed neither grace nor honour. One must be wary when dealing with such a man, slippery as an eel as he seemed to be: charm mattered nothing, after all. William Garbh's mouth firmed ominously.

Some time previously, when the sound of women's wailing for the drowned boy at Bolton had hardly had time to die away, a young man, with blond hair that was almost white, took horse, and galloped away from the scene of requiem, making north. The remembrance of the wan young corpse with green water-weed still tangled in his hair, last heir of Duncan II, affected him not with sorrow but with a fierce hope. He himself was the dead boy's eldest bastard half-brother, one of the many sons got by William Fitzduncan outside his Norman marriage. He himself, young Donald, of the blood of Lady Ingebjorg, first wife of Malcolm Ceann Mór, could call himself heir to Scotland as much and more as the young girl-boy anointed on the Stone of Scone at twelve years old. He, Donald, younger of the name, would find support in Moray, in the Orkneys, maybe also in Galloway which had Norse families living in enclaves near its coasts. All that was needed was a strong leader among them. The Boy of Egremont would never have made such a one, being guarded from the beginning by his tutors on their father's instructions and never allowed to stray in his own mind. Now, here was himself, watched and heeded so far by nobody. He would find the places, and the folk, who regarded the sons of Margaret the second wife of Malcolm III as Sassunach usurpers; his father William Fitzduncan, rightful heir to the throne, had remained weakly their servant, even calling out against de Brus of Annandale for trying to avoid battle that time with the English at Northallerton beneath the Standard, so that de Brus had turned coat for the sake of his English lands and had gone away to fight for the other side. Yet his, Donald's, father had been the son of the murdered Duncan II, rightful King of Scots; why should he have fought as he had for David Margaretson and thereafter been his loyal servitor? Now, one's own very colouring stood in one's favour; he would call himself Donald Bán in the north, after the old blinded king true Celts remembered, with the latter's descent still existing by way of the daughter married in Tynedale, and her daughter: but one need say little of that and instead, raise sons of one's own. This Malcolm men still called the Maiden had taken, they said, a vow of virginity. Donald Bán sneered. All of Margaret Atheling's descent had had monkish ways. Not so he.

He rode through the hills by the old Roman road, then took to unknown paths. He was thinking now that these Normans believed in surnames; well, he would take one for himself. His father had been William Fitzduncan and he himself would be MacWilliam, Son of William. Donald Bán MacWilliam. He would be heard of again in the south parts, and his sons after him. He rode now out of sound and sight as the dark hills closed about him, while far to the south-west they buried with sorrow the drowned boy of Egremont, last true heir of the old race.

The Scots Court heard in the following year of the magnificent embassy sent to France by King Henry II's Chancellor, Thomas Becket. This was a man of humble origins, tall and darkly handsome, learned by his own constant application in the household of a patron bishop, and said to possess great charm; the young Prince Henry – Eleanor of Aquitaine had, in this second marriage, produced a son a year – who had been put in Becket's charge as his tutor, adored him. As for Henry himself, who never stood on ceremony, he had been known to ride his horse into the great hall where his Chancellor dined in state, dismount and vault across the loaded table to share in the meal like any hungry man. It was whispered that, perhaps, he mocked the Chancellor's grandeur in such ways.

Now, this itself was manifest to all, and the King of England's power with it. Two hundred and fifty men on foot had advanced lately into Paris, singing, followed by the Chancellor's hounds and greyhounds, leashed and led by their keepers. Following these again were eight great waggons drawn by chargers, two of the waggons full of barrels of English ale, while the rest contained Becket's gear. Chained mastiffs, famous in England since Roman times, guarded each waggon, and on the back of every charger, as if to mock its strength, sat a monkey. Behind all of that again came twenty-eight packhorses with gold and silver plate, money and books – Becket never travelled without his library –, twenty-four changes of ceremonial raiment, and the Chancellor's portable altar and mass-vessels. Two hundred of his retinue followed; esquires bearing the shields of their knights who rode, mounted, led accordingly by the rein; then the falconers with hawks on their wrists; then lastly the young sons of barons whom the Chancellor had in his household.

'King Henry did not risk sending his own son among them to visit his wife's former husband,' remarked William Garbh drily: he was old enough by now to put two and two together.

'We are not done yet,' said Malcolm, who was relating it all. 'There followed still the clerks and stewards and servants, riding two by two. Last of all Becket himself came, chatting to friends. They say the whole town hurried out to see him.' The King of Scots sounded wistful; he himself had no such splendour, or not yet.

'They will agree,' said Countess Ada quietly, 'that a ruler powerful enough to send such an ambassador is fit for alliance with King Louis' daughter by his second wife, the child being still in the cradle. They mean her for little Prince Henry.'

'Well, they could hardly have sent one of the daughters by Louis' first,' muttered Garbh. 'I wager Henry asks for the whole of the Vexin as dowry; that is his aim. You yourself, my brother, should be looking for a wife abroad, with money and lands.'

Malcolm IV looked down his nose. Although he knew very well that his mother and the people of Lothian, who had often begged for it, wished him to marry, he had his head full of the counsels of Clairvaux, the gestes of Arthur and the undying legend of Edward the Confessor, on whom all the descendants of Margaret Atheling had been taught from the beginning to model themselves. There were likewise the Templars, whose recent institution Malcolm admired greatly; and a Templar also was celibate.

'I have taken a vow otherwise,' he murmured, and William Garbh burst out impatiently.

'What good is a vow against making heirs? The Confessor

could not contrive it, or so they say; he was forced to wed
Godwin's daughter for the sake of policy, but did nothing with
her, and pretended it was because of his vow.'

'They say he will be made a saint,' said Malcolm, shocked.

'Maybe, but had he been a whit less saintly there would have
been heirs to England, and we ourselves would have lived at
peace with them, being our own kin.' He reflected however that
at that rate, Margaret Atheling might never have had to reach
Scotland by sea, intending at the time to return to her mother's
folk in Hungary, but diverted by the storm.

'Well, well, it is old history now,' said Countess Ada. She was
watching her son Malcolm; for the sake of the kingdom, it
seemed a pity that he had taken these notions into his head. It
was true that there was William Garbh, and his brother David
who showed no signs of monkish inclinations either: but the
situation was not according to her own way of thinking, and
long ago she had cured her sons' father of it; Earl Henry had
ended by loving her. She closed her eyes for instants,
remembering. It would help Malcolm greatly were he to know
such love.

Malcolm meantime had turned away, discomfited. He was
still unaware that, shortly now, the opportunity to show
splendour to all the world would come, in fact within the year.
He was commanded shortly, as vassal for the English lands –
and it angered the Scots lords greatly that this should be so – to
attend King Henry in his siege of the town of Toulouse,
supposedly on behalf of Queen Eleanor, whose kinsman held it
against her. Malcolm determined to go, and to echo Becket's
embassy in glory as far as he might. All the world would be at
Toulouse; and perhaps this time King Henry would make him
a knight. He must on no account be absent from such an
occasion. Despite the murmurings of his lords, the King of
Scots fitted out a fleet of forty-five ships, new and gallant with
white ropes and sails painted with devices. Malcolm himself
strode about, long yellow hair flying beneath his helmet, to
inspect the rigging and victualling for so long a voyage, longer
than any he had ever made in his life. William Garbh would of
course accompany him; they might fall out at times, but were
after all companions. David was too young to go, but it could be
said to my lords that if any accident such as that of the White
Ship happened, there was a successor left among them, behind
in Scotland.

* * *

Young David in fact stood and watched, in chagrin because he was not going with his elder brothers, beside their mother the Countess and the two girls as the King's great fleet set sail. Margaret, the second sister and the most beautiful, was shortly to go to Brittany as the Duke's bride there, and had already begun to fill her dower-chest: placid Ada would go later on into Holland. They also would have to embark on ships, less grand than these, and risk the grey unpredictable crossing. How handsome Malcolm had looked in his shining armour! He would certainly be foremost among everyone at Toulouse.

'Do you suppose, mother, that this time King Henry will make my brother a knight?' Margaret hardly dared ask the Countess, queenly in her long robes stirred by the shore wind, and the widow's veil she always wore beneath her circlet. Ada however answered this enquiring daughter gently.

'I know that the King will break his heart if it does not happen, so you must say your prayers.' She herself would also say them for the fleet's safety: in her opinion it need never have set out.

Out to sea at last, William Garbh sat in the bows, watching the ploughing of the summer water. Now that they had veered to leeward and the land had been left behind, the sea was blue in colour, a foretaste of the unknown lands of the south. He had after all not travelled beyond his own country since the time long ago at Lewes. It was intriguing to look forward to the prospect of a foreign land, the chatter of the Provençals in their *langue d'oc*, the sight of the very towers of Toulouse itself, key to the Mediterranean for any inland trade. Behind him, the young nobles who had come with the King continued their high French talk; he, William, took no part. He would always be by himself, in such ways.

He watched the sea, thinking of a thing which had happened to him shortly before he left. Maidenhead; he had lost his, and had no regrets. It was to be cherished, no doubt, as a sign of chastity since Pope Hildebrand had issued his edict to the clergy forbidding them to marry, but all that had happened was that the clergy now kept mistresses and fathered bastards; a man had to live naturally. As for the legend about the magic horn from which only one knight of true chastity could drink at court unscathed, Malcolm might drink from it if he would; oneself would not attempt it. There was the old curse of Donald Bán, unforgotten; but it made no difference whether or not one lived like a monk, it would come or else it would fail. William himself would live, he had already decided, as a man.

A musician struck up on board the King's ship soon, with a troubadour lay such as they had in Queen Eleanor's duchy. William had no illusions about troubadours; they were, he knew already, men who loved other men. King William Rufus had been one such. William stared now at his brother's exquisite profile, raised to the mast as the music flowed by. The sail flapped, with the old familiar sign of the dragon painted on it. Malcolm – it had become impossible to suggest anything of the kind, the King took offence nowadays very easily – had not even adopted the new de Warenne wyvern, the dragon with eagle's wings to which the family had a right since Fat William – he would also be at Toulouse – had inherited the Honour of the Eagle, the lands of Pevensey first won at Hastings by a noble who had disturbed an eagle's nest to build his castle in Normandy, and by this time had left no heirs of his own line.

The dragon. He himself, William, would like a ship with a lion on its sails; a lion in gules on or, a lion rampant. It had been his dream since a boy, and the lion to be on his pennants also, waving in the breeze when he rode down again to Northumbria; but when would that be? It depended on Malcolm and his vassalage to Henry, whom he evidently admired more than did oneself: but my lords, on return, would cause trouble of some kind. It was difficult to picture Malcolm as anything but young, with the fabled beauty of the Athelings and of Earl Waltheof. He himself, William de Warenne – it was the only surname they possessed – was a plain great clumsy Norman.

The English coast came in sight long before the light failed, then the slow dusk came on and lanterns were lit at the masthead below the flapping dragon. The King of Scots' fleet drifted on, jewelled against the night, towards France and Toulouse, and presently the music fell silent and most men slept, wearing their armour. It seemed a long way to go for a quarrel not one's own.

Two

Henry of Anjou, King of England, Duke of Normandy and ruler in his wife's right of Aquitaine, sat on his dais in the appointed field at Quercy in Périgord, having withdrawn lately from Toulouse after some weeks of siege. The necessity irritated Henry, who was a man of impatient temper but also, prudent. Although he preferred a tidy ending to any war – he had been successful, in the end, as all would agree, in England – it had not been politic to continue this one while his overlord, Louis VII of France, elected to remain, ostensibly guarding his sister, inside the besieged town in person. The apologetic monarch – two daughters got out of Eleanor in fourteen years in the marriage bed, whereas oneself had achieved a posse of sons in seven – had at first come to try to mediate, as he put it, between Henry, his own vassal for Normandy, and Raymond of St. Gilles, who held the town in despite of his cousin Eleanor and in her absence. Raymond was by now married to Louis' sister Constance, who – it was at other times diverting to unravel the web of family relationships, but not now – had in former times been the wife of King Stephen's son Eustace, the same young man who had conveniently choked to death after setting fire to a field of monks' corn near Bury. Now, Constance and her royal brother Louis were both cooped up in Toulouse, the talks having come to nothing although, for two men married at different times to the same woman, both kings had parted in surprising amity. Henry permitted himself a brief recollection of Eleanor's indescribable charm, of which even he was not yet sated, senior to him as she might be; such a woman would never in any case be conquered by old age. He did not love her and never had, but it flattered him to be her husband.

Now, there had been this general enforced withdrawal. Henry tried to console himself by surveying the massed army of chivalry which had accompanied him from all points in the first

instance by sea and land. There were English barons, the great
lords of Normandy and Anjou, the Bretons, subdued for a time
and prepared, as they seldom were, to fight under the orders of
a stranger; the lords of Aquitaine who supported Duchess
Eleanor's right; and not least, accompanied by his *farouche*
brother William and an elegant retinue, the beautiful young
King of Scots. One would atone for the humiliation of refusing
the boy a knighthood two years ago by granting it to him now;
Malcolm, together with a Welsh prince who had also come, had
no doubt learned his lesson. All of these young men, about to
be made knights by his, Henry's, own hand, had kept vigil the
whole of last night, kneeling throughout in full armour before
an altar raised on the field. Henry himself had slept in his tent
as usual, with his short Angevin cloak wrapped about him.
Now, he was ready for the knighting ceremony, watched by all
eyes in the glittering field; he, the son of the royal woman the
English had once cast out, causing her to escape in the snow!
To bring England to heel since then had been a pleasure as well
as a duty. It resembled his marriage; he would never love it, but
savoured its possession.

Pennants – it was beginning to be the fashion to design and
display one's coat of arms – waved colourfully before the silk
tents, the sun shone as always here, and everything conspired
to show the world his, Henry's, power. He knew he ruled more
lands in France now than Louis his overlord, and Louis knew it
also, trapped as he was within the walls of Toulouse and as
usual uncertain what would happen next. Soon, one's young
son Henry should marry the child Marguerite of France, Louis'
daughter; that would bring in the Vexin. One need not, after
all, trouble too greatly about the late necessity of withdrawal
from Toulouse: it would come to heel in time. The King of
England set himself to appear gracious, aware of his own
undoubted charm, which had nothing to do with beauty.

He drew his sword. It was the arranged signal for the young
King of Scots to come forward and kneel before him, the first
to be dubbed knight. Malcolm the Maiden advanced, slender
and fair in bright armour at nineteen. Henry found it in him to
admire the delicate loveliness he himself would never possess;
but it would not, he had already decided, make old bones.
Malcolm knelt, in token of vassalage, meantime only for
Huntingdon, but this was not the moment to say so aloud.
Henry's voice was itself unequivocal and clear as he laid his

sword on the young man's shoulder.

'Arise, Sire Malcolm de Varenne, King of Scots.'

The Maiden rose, flushed with pleasure, a true knight at last. He knew already that their mother's surname was the only one he and William and David possessed: and William was waiting now behind him. William had kept his vigil also and was to be made a knight; but then a thing happened that neither king had foreseen.

William Garbh, lips set and steady, bowed briefly to King Henry; he would not have it said afterwards that he had ignored the Plantagenet. Then he knelt, not to the King of England but to the King of Scots: a knight now, fit to fashion other knights. William's voice was as clear as Henry's had been, and rang out over the field.

'My brother and liege lord of Scotland, I pray you dub me knight.'

There was an instant's hush, then a murmur. Henry's gaze had grown pebble-hard, but he made no other sign. Nobody intercepted Malcolm's sword; it flashed out from the scabbard, silver in the sun of France; and rested briefly on William Garbh's mailed shoulder.

'Arise, Sire Guillaume de Varenne.'

Malcolm's voice was, as always, light, and held astonishment; ought he to have done this? It would however have humiliated William to refuse him; one knew within oneself how it felt. Malcolm raised his eyes, and beheld the not unfriendly gaze of Fat William of Boulogne, Cousin Isabel de Warenne's husband, who was here also and waiting – not before time, when one thought of it – to be made a knight with the rest. There was of course no question but that it would be done by King Henry: Malcolm moved aside. Nevertheless many of his followers, in some quiet glee at William Garbh's example, came and knelt instead to the King of Scots. Malcolm IV made thirty knights that day.

Afterwards everyone went to the feasting, welcome after the long night's vigil and the waiting in full armour in the hot sun. Relations appeared pleasant, with King Malcolm seated on King Henry's right. It was observed, however, that there was a certain wicked tautness about the Angevin's mouth which came there often when Henry FitzEmpress was angry; and that it was to be seen when he looked in the direction of Sire Guillaume de Varenne, knight.

* * *

News reached them in Scotland soon of all of it, also that a great sickness had broken out in the French camp, it being summer. Countess Ada was alarmed for the King. Fat William, Stephen's son, perished of it overnight, his new knighthood availing him nothing. 'He will leave a well-dowered widow in your niece Isabel,' said Alice Fitzduncan. 'King Henry will waste no time in finding her a husband of his choice.'

Ada remembered hearing that yet another William, Henry's own younger brother, a Plantagenet, was already passionately in love with Isabel of Warren and Surrey; no doubt the Pope would be appealed to in the matter. Meantime, there was no doubt that the King of Scots himself must come home; my lords clamoured for it in any case, and there was uprising again in Galloway. She pressed King David's silver coins – he had been first to mint such things in Scotland – on a messenger, and sent him in haste abroad; it was no reflection on the King's courage and his brother's to return when an outbreak of sickness was raging. Prudence dictated that they must do so, however unwillingly.

A sulky Malcolm returned, accompanied by William Garbh and such of his own followers as had not succumbed to the great sickness. Trouble awaited. Six of his rebellious earls, only one out of seven remaining faithful, chased him into Perth and held him captive there; they were incensed over the situation regarding England and the rumour that Malcolm intended going shortly to aid King Henry in subduing Wales. 'Mind your own kingdom,' they shouted from beneath the walls. 'We are no vassals! Scotland is free!'

Ada the Countess, informed, wrote frantically for aid in every possible direction; to Abbot Ailred, her husband's boyhood friend whom she had long since made her own; to the monks of Durham, the Archbishop of St. Andrews, anyone else she could hope to convene in the matter. The only way to placate the rebels was, she knew, by way of the Church, which they respected; to have recourse to arms would bring disaster; there was already enough unrest in the realm following the King's absence. Her instinct proved correct; finally Malcolm, shut in his own castle somewhat as King Louis had been at Toulouse, was induced to make peace, and the nobles also. Only Earl Ferteth of Menteith, who was having troubles of his own as regarded a Celtic claimant to his title, continued to growl. 'Keep to your own realm, and let Henry mind his. He has taken enough upon himself; let his own aid him, if they will.'

Malcolm let it be known that he had been brought to a good understanding in general by way of the churchmen. He was contemplating the endowment of a new abbey at Cupar, after the manner of his grandfather. Meantime, the body of poor Fat William had been brought home to England and with almost indecent delay, the remarriage of his widow was arranged. King Henry's lovesick brother, William Plantagenet, was not permitted to hope for very long; the Pope refused the claim on the grounds of consanguinity, and young William withdrew thereafter to his mother's court at Rouen, there to pine away and die after news came that his beloved, and well-dowered, Isabel had been married instead to his and the King's brutal half-brother, dead Geoffrey's bastard, Hameline Plantagenet.

'*He* will not fail to give her children at once,' murmured Alice Fitzduncan. 'He has their father Geoffrey's propensities. Such a handsome young man, Geoffrey, I remember, in his black surcoat sewn with gold leopards which he affected, but they should never have married a boy of fifteen to the Empress at twenty-six, especially after a first husband old enough to have been her grandfather, with whom they say she was happy enough.'

'One does not die of a broken heart,' put in Ada the Countess. 'Young William Plantagenet must have had something else the matter.' But Alice did not hear; her eyes had grown sad and remote, as happened often since the drowning of her own William, the Boy of Egremont, the only male child she had ever borne her husband: she knew Fitzduncan had many bastards, who lived on.

Meantime, the King fought well in Galloway, subduing it for the time. Old Fergus its lord – his wife was another of Henry I's daughters on the wrong side of the blanket – retired to King David's Abbey of the Holy Rood as a monk, but died the year following. His sons Uchtred and Gilbert, who had never dealt together, were left as usual making war. The King then went off with Henry II to Wales, as he had earlier promised; there was less opposition from my lords than before Malcolm's valiant fighting in Galloway and, later, Moray: but the continued obedience to England was unpopular nevertheless. 'Why should our King serve theirs?' they growled. It was the hero-worship of an eager boy for a masterful character which had begun it all: Henry FitzEmpress often achieved victory in such ways.

Malcolm however fell grievously sick at Doncaster. Ada

recalled with anguish Earl Henry's own frequent illnesses: her remembered husband, 'the pride of youth, the glory of knights, the joy of young men.' Now there was no monk Malachy to lay his hands on Henry's son and heal him. If only Malcolm would forgo his monkish vow, and marry, or at least fall in love! It seemed unnatural that he should leave no heir behind.

Three

The King's mother Ada was escorted into church for the Cupar consecration by one Berowald the Fleming, in his broad hat and chain: he had ridden down especially from Moray, a province he and his fellow-settlers had made by now, in only three years after the King's grant, more peaceful than they found it. In fact so grateful were the inhabitants to the King for having made peace in those parts that when one of the pretenders, a MacHeth, had been released from prison with a promise, well enough meant, of being given Ross to govern, the inhabitants had set upon him as he came north amusing himself with minstrels and jugglers, seized him, and blinded and castrated him without hesitation. It was too late, however, as the man already had sons. He had, Berowald reflected, however been sent to a monastery in the south, there to end his days; and was reported to sit daily in the sun there saying that had they left him but the eye of a sparrow, he would show them what he could do to them in return. There it was; and he himself, having overcome the bloodthirsty reputation of mercenaries from the Low Countries in Stephen's time, had settled down to a thriving trade with wool from the well-fed sheep in those green flat northern places, as his countrymen were also doing, since the time of old King Henry Beauclerc, in Wales near the coast.

He thought of the damp Welsh valleys now, watching the wasted figure of King Malcolm come in procession, carrying a candle; the young King might, the Fleming thought, be wearing his own shroud. His shrewd eyes slid sideways to where Ada the Countess knelt by him, but her expression told him nothing although she must know well enough that her son was dying at twenty-three. William Garbh, substance behind the shadow, followed; for some time he had been warden of the kingdom by reason of his brother's health. The King had nevertheless fought Somerled, that subterranean half-glimpsed

77

lion among the heather, at the beginning and now at the end, at last, of his reign; a hundred and eighty-four galleys had sailed in defiance lately up the Clyde, bearing fifteen thousand fighting men from Argyll and Man and the Sudreys, of which by now Somerled called himself king. He had gathered power with cunning, having married the King of Norway's daughter, and had by her a daughter who in turn had married MacHeth. The Fleming's precise mind tallied it all up. The end had been nothing, for Somerled had been murdered, they said, in his tent at Renfrew, for which they blamed the King; but the King had killed the son in open battle. There were too many pretenders still, however; the MacHeths and MacWilliams would give trouble beyond the span of any man's life.

Ada the Countess tried to listen to the chanting. It seemed that she had knelt in so many new-built abbeys, watching in the end husband, father-in-law, son all die; and now her daughters were gone overseas, although the marriage of both seemed happy. Young David was in the south, having been demanded as a hostage by King Henry. The lad had not minded going; he was like William Garbh, hot for adventure, and he wanted to experience the life of the English Court, though the splendour of Becket was to be seen no more; Becket was a churchman now, and unfriends with King Henry. How things changed! She was beginning to be achingly lonely, as she had been when Earl Henry died. She thought again of her daughters. Young Ada was married two years since to her Count of Holland, and had children; Margaret, the more beautiful of the two, before that to Brittany, having lately given birth to a little girl she and Duke Conan had called Constance and who was said to be more beautiful than any. Of what use was beauty if it died? Margaret however seemed content; she loved her husband, and Brittany itself was, evidently, like parts of Scotland, being likewise a part of ancient Lyonnesse with even the tongue similar to Gaelic. The wild kerns there were like the folk of the north in more than speech; one local lord from Finistère was so unruly he had been sent on crusade with his wife, who was as wild as he. Ralph her brother brought all such news, riding as he still did back and forth upon the earth, evidently desiring neither wife nor home. He would be here again soon, and Ada craved his company. The good Fleming was dutiful, and had made a success of the venture up in Moray, but his company was somewhat dull.

She turned her attention to the altar, and what was

proceeding there as the Host was raised. For some reason, as her mind wandered again, she thought of the long-dead King Alexander, who had led an Arab horse up in gift with trappings of silver, a sword and shield, and a suit of Turkish armour. They were gone, the days of splendour, the days of the matchless pearls of Queen Sibylla. She heard the King give his short dry cough. It reminded her, frighteningly, of his father's.

'And so, my sister, as Reynald says who was himself there, it was worse this time in its way than at Clarendon. Becket the Archbishop is the same man after all as Becket the Chancellor, proud as the devil. On that earlier occasion, my lords broke down the door of the room where the clerics were seated, and flung back their cloaks to brandish their fists in Becket's face.'

'Why? That would never be permitted to happen here.' Ada continued with her stitching while Alice, as had been the way of things in England, hooked at the stitches neatly from the back while her daughter Amabilis sat sorting and handing the silks. Through the door-curtain, the murmuring of the other women sounded. Ralph continued with his tale as though Alice had not spoken; like many ageing persons, he was content with the sound of his own voice and preferred to listen to no other.

'Why? Because he has crossed the King's will. They say he would have carried his crucifix barefoot at Clarendon, for the sake of show, but was prevented. As he went out of the Council, he tripped on a faggot, and was mocked for a traitor, and Hameline, Isabel's husband, joined in as loud as any. Becket turned on Hameline in the old way and swore that if it were not for his cloth, he would show which was the traitor. They say now, though the King has had the ports watched, that Becket is fled abroad despite him. What may come of it all, God knows.'

Ralph quaffed his ale, which Ada always had specially brought up for him from the south. His hair had thinned and he had lost some teeth; they were both growing older. They sat, with Alice, in the solar at Haddington, the town Ada herself had founded and where now, with the increasing ache in her bones, she preferred to stay, writing about them always to the monks at Durham to ask for their prayers to help her endurance of that and other ills. It had long been in her mind that she would like to see an abbey built here finer than at Cupar, shedding its light over Lothian like a lamp. The Lamp of Lothian. Ralph was still talking on.

'This affair of the courts may have wider results than anyone thinks yet. The King is right in certain parts of the matter. One cleric raped a young woman after killing her father. Another elsewhere committed murder. Are these to be let off with a light sentence or a fine because the bishops will not be put to the expense of keeping 'em in their own prisons? The King's justice is harsh, but can be deserved as much by those as by any. All men are no more than human.'

'It is a matter for the Pope, no doubt,' put in Alice again. Ada said nothing; Rome was far away, and the cruel business of Isabel's forced marriage had been caused by delay there. She heard Ralph snort.

'The Pope fears an anti-pope, and kings may use their power of election to sway him by such means as they will. Temporal matters need temporal remedies.' He was becoming ponderous with the ale. 'I myself,' he said, 'would not molest Thomas Becket in his see of Canterbury, but there are many who would, and will if he should ever return to England.'

'Maybe poverty abroad will cause him to vacate his see.'

Ada reflected that it was a long way from the grand train that early time into Paris, with monkeys sitting on the Chancellor's horses. Everything changed, as she had already told herself. It was a long time now since Earl Henry had died. How old was she? How long would she have to live on, after watching her children die?

The Lamp of Lothian. It could rival even Lewes. It could be remembered to all generations, and it would fill her old age to begin it: at Haddington, her own town: Haddington Abbey, the Lamp of Lothian, famous for all time.

Four

William Garbh, Warden of Scotland, was lying with a young woman in the late autumn bracken. She was a serving-maid at Slipperfield, a place of Comyn's and Histilla's which his mother often frequented, and who had for some time now flaunted her tail and then kept running away. He had caught her at last and pinned her down here, where it was private. The high coarse stems, darkening now with their side-shoots long uncurled, still enabled William to see the road; his mind was no longer on the girl, having achieved her. It was growing cold, now he thought of it; so was he. He thumbed her bared thighs, then covered them considerately with the folds of his tunic. Provided a woman was young, clean and willing, it was all he asked. He had two bastards already, one by Avenel's daughter over in Eskdale; his mother was fond of the little girl and had called her Isabel. That might have been for her own mother, or for her niece married now to Hameline Plantagenet and sent across to Normandy, where her husband kept ward for King Henry. Henry had been equally brutal as regarded Fat William's sister Mary, an abbess whom he had likewise married off forcibly to an Angevin bridegroom. The Boulogne title could still be inconvenient, but the abbess, though made swiftly pregnant by the Angevin, was petitioning the Pope to be allowed to return to her convent. One heard most such tidings by way of uncle Ralph.

William raised his head now, hearing a horseman come along the road that wound below Yair Hill. He was a slim fair man in mail, yellow hair flying below the helm. It was the King, with his vizor raised. William wondered why his brother rode alone; it was unusual and, in Malcolm's weak state, not safe. Allowing his curiosity, and watchfulness, to get the better of him he rose from the girl, who had been beginning to respond; she cried out in reproach as the strong warm big-boned body left hers.

'Be here again tomorrow and we will do the like,' he told her curtly: she might please herself either way, he no longer cared. He went to where his palfrey waited among the trees. He had determined to follow Malcolm for the latter's own sake: the things a King did were as a rule done publicly, with royal pomp or else a parade of churchmen; but this King was also his brother. He had been making towards Innerleithen priory, and having gone so far William followed him. It would be an opportunity, which he seldom had these days, for them to have a word alone. He himself was occupied with affairs of state which had been delegated to him, and with calming down the anger still felt over the Welsh expedition, which had finally ruined the King's health, and was in any case a further sign of English servitude.

There was a lay-brother at the gate, where Malcolm's mount also waited. William cast the reins he held to the man also, dismounted and went in: behind him the river ran high with late rain, though the bracken, he recalled, had been fairly dry. The brother, who knew him, murmured that the King was in the chapel. He seemed to stare at the ground over some solemn matter; one would discover it, no doubt.

The flicker of candles met Garbh, the sight of a kneeling figure and the sound of sobbing. There was a small coffin, a child's, set before the altar. Nobody else was in the church except for the unseen monks, chanting the Office by custom behind their screen. Garbh went and laid a hand on his brother's shoulder. The King turned a face to him that was flushed, and already swollen with tears.

'My son died yesterday,' Malcolm said. 'I did not hear in time to come to him.'

Afterwards they walked out of the small church together; it was long since they had been as close. William asked who the child's mother had been.

'It does not matter. She is dead. She died at the birth.'

He began then to talk about the little child, a son, of whom he had been fond. It had been old enough to run to him. 'They looked after him here,' Malcolm said. 'I will have a place of sanctuary ordained in his memory. It is all I can do for him, that and the masses. He committed no sin, as I myself did in breaking my celibate's vow.'

'There is no sin in being natural. Your vow was hardly so.' William was aware that he spoke against the tendencies of the Church nowadays, soaked as it had become in the thought of

Bernard of Clairvaux the so-called mellifluous doctor: he himself had never liked what he had heard of the man, and considered that Bernard's harshnesses had done as much harm as his good. The Maiden's face – he would always be remembered as the Maiden – turned to his brother, great eyes opened wide, remembering.

'Our mother plied me with wine once. There was a young girl serving it. I remember nothing more except that when I awoke, it was in the girl's bed. Later, mother told me there was to be the child. She was pleased. He looked like me, but I have lost my place among the virgin knights.' His voice was sad; as usual nowadays, he coughed at the end of speaking.

William refrained from the coarse rejoinder he would have made to anyone else. 'You will make your way to heaven, my brother, never fear,' he said roughly, and laid a hand on the sick man's arm. They returned together in silence, thinking of the child's requiem and of the coming place of sanctuary, with the river running always by and future generations puzzled about the fact of the Maiden's son. The question would recur in William's lifetime.

By December, with the bitter cold, Malcolm the King was dead. Watching the stricken face of their mother who knelt before the bier, William thought again of the ill charm of Donald Bán. It had struck down the beautiful King of Scots still in youth, and his unknown son likewise. Somewhere a clerk, remembering the dead boy's valiant fight against Somerled, the rebels of Moray and Galloway, the MacHeth pretenders and the men of Ross, was writing a poem, as had been written long ago about the first Ceann Mór, the Great Chief, father to nine sons; now, the title was given to his dead great-grandson after him. *Malcolm Ceann Mór, Great Head, son of Henry, the High King of Alban, the best Christian that was to the Gael on the east side of the sea, for almsgiving and fasting and devotion, died.*

He, William, was now King of Scots.

They anointed and crowned him at Scone on Christmas Eve. He saw the blaze of candles ready to celebrate Christ's birth, and felt under him the hardness of the sacred stone beneath its splendid cloths and, on his body in four given places, the warm trickle of the holy oil that made him different from all other men as long as he should live. He felt the cold rim of Malcolm's gold crown press down on his brow. He would not be a beautiful king like his brother, or a virgin one; he would marry when it suited him, though not before, and the marriage should be a grand one from abroad, maybe from France. He would have the lion on his standard, the lion of Scotland, gules on or within its containing tressure. He would be known by this rampant lion; it should wave again in Northumbria, the land his grandfather had given him long ago, and in the other debated lands Henry FitzEmpress had obtained by breaking his word. He would let the King of England gainsay him in no way, would do homage only for what was due, namely Huntingdon. He would go to Normandy next year, as Henry had already demanded, but as no vassal, only a fellow-king; Henry himself was likewise vassal to France. All such things must be clearly understood, and he, William, would make them clear, as he had done that time of the knighting at Périgord. A hard rival needed a firm hand, a swift mind and a strong sword. He had all those, he, William, the Lion of Scotland. The name pleased him.

He heard the Archbishop continue mass, having done with the anointing and crowning. Tomorrow, Christmas Day, would see the grand feast for the beginning of his reign, and Christ's birth. He himself was twenty-two, and his health was excellent.

Five

'And so, brother and liege – this happened at Caen, I believe –
they were speaking of you together, King Henry and his
adherents, not favourably for whatever reason, and Richard du
Homet, an honest knight I've met at Woodstock, manfully
defended you and angered the devil's descendant, who then
burst out, in the way he has, to the effect that you are a manifest
traitor.'

'Traitor to whom?' said William. 'I owe Henry nothing, save
Huntingdon.' He recalled the hard glint in the King of
England's eye that time at Périgord: it might be that
unforgotten affront to English dignity, or else his own tentative
recent relations opened with Louis of France. 'I have enfeoffed
you in Huntingdon,' he said to David his brother, now
returned, casually clad as they were wont now to be at the
English Court, in a short Angevin cloak and belted tunic like
Henry himself. David resembled oneself, however, physically
and also in nature, more so than poor Malcolm, dead now over
a year. William briefly recalled the relation he had had of a
vision vouchsafed to one Richard the Clerk by the late King, the
night after Malcolm's death; Malcolm had appeared to Richard
in shining raiment, and when asked why, stated that it was
because he had undergone death still a virgin. Either the clerk's
imagination had been running away with him – he might after
all have seen somebody else in the vision – or Malcolm had, not
after all having lost his virginity with deliberate intent, been
admitted to the ranks of the elect as though he had kept it.
William dismissed the matter from his mind.

David continued with the purveying of gossip from Caen.
'Henry then,' he said, 'behaved in the manner he always does
when crossed, incredible in any other man; he pulled his cap
from his head, his belt off likewise, threw off his cloak and, they
say, his clothes, grabbed the very silk coverlet off the couch
whereon he sat, and having done all that sat chewing a piece of

straw off the floor on your account, like a man half mad. I will say I did not find him so in England; at Court it was even dull, a trifle.'

He laughed suddenly. 'He is not altogether unlikeable,' he said. 'You know the story of Hugh of Witham? – they speak of him for the see of Lincoln soon – with whom Henry was enraged as, evidently, of late with yourself; that other was however for denying Communion to some forester, God knows why. Churchman Hugh wanted a word with him, but the King took horse and galloped off in a temper into the forest, with his courtiers after him. The good Hugh pursued them and found Henry sitting at last on the ground beneath a tree. He sat down beside him – there was a silence, as you may imagine – and King Henry, who after all cannot bear inaction at any time, started to sew with a needle and thread at a leather stall for his finger, as he'd injured it. 'How like your cousins of Falaise you look!' Hugh remarked, and King Henry suddenly roared with laughter and began to roll about on the ground. The cousins, as you know, were tanners of Falaise, old William of Normandy's mother's stock, and he a bastard. Not every monarch would have laughed or rolled on the ground for such a reason.'

William grunted. The word Falaise seemed to have some hidden echo, some meaning he preferred not to fathom. Perhaps he had heard it at some unfavourable time, and had forgotten. He rose.

'Perhaps Henry will laugh less often when he has crowned his son King in his lifetime, as he intends,' he said. 'They will talk then of the Young King and the Old, and that will not please him.'

'Do not imitate the custom when you yourself have a son: but it has been done before, in France and Germany and, I believe, with Charlemagne, but his sons had not the spirit of Henry's surviving four by Eleanor. Geoffrey I like not; he is sly, and so is little John the King's favourite. Young Henry has nothing in his head; his French wife Marguerite is wiser than he.'

'I like it not that the sly brother should be betrothed to our niece Constance, with Brittany firmly in mind.'

'Well, since Conan's trouble she and our sister Margaret are beholden to the King. As regards the other sons, Richard is to govern Poitou, young Henry a part of Normandy and maybe the Vexin: there is nothing yet for John, and so his father jests and calls him Lackland.'

William scowled. The King of France's second daughter Alais

had been betrothed lately to Henry's son Richard, whose elder brother had already married her sister: William had secretly hoped for the French alliance for himself.

'Come, let us go and drink wine,' he said, and they rose and went together to where it stood, poured, and drank together. 'No doubt,' remarked David of Huntingdon, 'the King will invite us both to attend his son's crowning at Westminster or Winchester, whichever is decided on in the end. It would hardly be courteous did he not do so. Perhaps, however, when he sees you ride in, my liege, he will chew straw once again in sight of all.'

David grinned. He was, still and forever, a year younger than the King, and so free as yet of responsibility; and, in his turn by now, twenty-two.

Earlier that year the King of Scots, with a Norway hawk on his wrist, had ridden beyond the flat lands below Bellencombre, the de Warenne stronghold in Normandy. He had left King Henry raging at the supposed incompetence of his wife Eleanor, whom he had left briefly in charge while he was occupied elsewhere; as a result, he had returned to raze castles, in particular Fougères. William had ridden away from it all after distinguishing himself in a tournament at Valennes, to visit his kinswoman Isabel and her husband Hameline the King's half-brother, whom he continued to dislike. Hameline was riding beyond the bounds now on the King's business, and William was glad to be alone. He let the hawk flutter upwards, above where the Varenne river wound as it had done from the beginning, before the time when flat-bottomed boats had anchored up in the shallows to exchange merchandise and make the dwellers on the land rich from the Bronze Age, when there were still mammoth and reindeer to be trapped in the swamps here for meat. Then the Romans had come: then the Danes at last in their long ships with the dragon prows, handfasting the tall de Varenne women with their Roman blood: and a son of such handfasting had been old Herfast the Dane, who had several fair sisters. One had been Gunnor, who had ensnared Duke Richard the Fearless of Normandy. Thence, from Duchess Gunnor and the later marriage of William de Warenne to the Conqueror's daughter, had come titles and power and, as with himself now, kingship; but to the Normans and the King of France he remained Guillaume de Varenne.

That morning, he had walked with his cousin Isabel on the ramparts; she was big with child again and two hard-mouthed brats of Hameline's were already in the nursery. She had made a bitter mouth for herself, walking always with her pet genet which curved against her feet, its great eyes watchful and luminous. 'I have had, as you see, cousin, to submit to the appetites of my second husband in a way the first would never have demanded of me. I am told by him that King Henry's way is always to marry heiresses to men of his own who will give them a child a year to occupy them, mind and body.'

The genet curved its spotted back. Isabel bent swiftly and stroked its fur, looking for instants like her old graceful self in the amiable years with Fat William. 'I am not the worst off,' she told him. 'Poor Mary of Boulogne, my former sister-in-law the Romsey abbess, has been brutally handled, ravished from her convent, married by force and got with child although she was by choice the bride of Christ. It is all to ensure that Boulogne itself does not become a centre for disobedience to Henry. The Flemish bridegroom he chose to force on Mary is allied, of course, to Anjou. The child – there is a second on the way, Henry's orders are thorough, believe me – will be loyal to him. Mary herself awaits the Pope's expected freeing of her to return at last to her vocation, but what has been done to her – and to me – is swifter than any proceedings at the Lateran; such matters take more time than ours.'

William had left her unhappy talk, had passed by her mother Ela crouching as always over the brazier in the solar – Ela's husband Patrick of Salisbury was in command now of the King's forces in Aquitaine, and Ela herself was again discontented – and had come out into the air. He felt that if he were to encounter Hameline his host, he would smash his face with one fist for the usage he made of Isabel. As for Mary of Boulogne, he remembered her as a plump kindly little creature on the long-ago ride to Chichester, among them all; she had not then been a nun, and greatly resembled her mother, Stephen's Queen Matilda. No doubt her Angevin ravisher found the plumpness delectable enough. It was a savage fate for such women, possessors of broad lands without protectors. Boulogne now, like England, was safe for Henry; like Brittany, where he had lately deposed one's brother-in-law Conan and betrothed his own seven-year-old son to the infant heiress. Everywhere, except in Scotland, the pattern was the same; and from Scotland itself Henry had wrested great swathes of land in the north by breaking his word. Malcolm had been young, had admired Henry and had hoped for early knighthood. He, William, was harder, older.

The hawk swooped, then pounced in mid-air, bringing down a dunlin. The latter's shrill swift pipe of alarm roused a soft widespread twittering from the nearby regions of the river nests. William retrieved and hooded the hawk, hung the bloodstained prey from his saddle-girth, and turned to perceive a horseman, alone except for a small following; the band seemed like merchants. The leader approached, and swept off his broad hat.

'You are the King of Scots,' he said in a low voice. 'I had not hoped to find you alone so readily.'

He was a Fleming, and known to Berowald, the man who had made peace in Moray in Malcolm's time. 'There was no means of bringing word to you out of France into Normandy except by such as myself,' he said. 'We merchants come and go even in time of war, though often set upon for what we carry.' He smiled. William stared at his face; it was honest, with hair cut squarely at the level of the ears. 'What would you with me?' he asked quietly. Hameline Plantagenet would soon enough ride home; he himself was watched always, as he knew well. This Fleming seemed of independent mind.

'Sire, I come from your kin of Vermandois, who are close about King Louis,' he said. 'As you know, the King's new wife bore him a son at last in the summer, and the marriage of a daughter with England is no longer of the import it was. Louis himself has endured many insults from King Henry, the refting of his first wife being the least of them: you know the rest, the story of Toulouse, of Fougères, of Andelys, Dol, Combourg, the South itself. There is also Becket, whom King Louis shelters and who will presently be at Sens. Thirdly – and a Vermandois as you know is the lover of Queen Eleanor's sister, and they love one another well – thirdly, there is another power the Queen trusts more than her husband nowadays: her uncle, Ralph de la Faye.

'This is the plan. Our King would thrust an army against the English coast at the same time as, were you willing, a spearhead of your own descended into Northumbria. All men know how you were deprived of it in your brother's day. To draw off attention from Normandy itself, which Louis hopes to regain, is of importance. This was a province of France; it is so no longer.'

William frowned. 'It is two centuries, or very near, since Rolf the Ganger became Patrician of Normandy,' he said. 'It will take much rooting out of Henry's barons here if such a war should come.'

'The war is already upon us. You have seen for yourself the vengeance Henry is taking at many places, though they say Andelys was vacated first on the advice of his mother at Rouen. The Empress will however not live long; when she dies, nothing will contain Henry's devil, greed. His wife's subjects loathe him, and they say by now so does she.'

'Some still love him, nevertheless. I believe Becket does so, enemies as they have outwardly become. How fares he?' He asked not out of any great tenderness for Becket, but to gain time. The project sounded feasible, but he could not commit himself without his lords' full agreement; he must return to Scotland, and sound out their hearts and minds.

'The Archbishop is in straits for money, as all know; and is petitioning the Pope to excommunicate England.' The merchant stretched out a hand in a white leather gauntlet. 'Do not fail France, sire. Remember that in the days of England's rightful ruler, your kinsman Edgar the Atheling, France would gladly have aided him and placed him on his throne again, ousting the Bastard, had Edgar been a man such as you are yourself.'

'We are as God made us,' growled William. Edgar the Atheling, brother of Margaret, had never become king of anything; his closest friendship had been with Curthose, and the Conqueror himself had not taken him seriously enough to do anything but use him gently once Edgar had made his peace after a shipwreck of all his rich gear of Ceann Mór's gift, and other mishaps. 'He was a man of no luck,' William murmured. 'I myself may be such another.'

'Nevertheless King Louis would be your friend; will you be his? The rest I have named are ready, and your kinsman Leicester also, in England.' Leicester had been one's grandmother Isabel de Vernandois' son by the first marriage. His wife Peronelle was an amazon: William remembered her with amusement.

'I do not refuse the hand of friendship, and you may say so to those who sent you,' he said. 'Go now; the leopards are returning.' Hameline Plantagenet and his following came in sight, flaunting the golden arms of Anjou quartered with Isabel's wyvern. Fat William was unforgotten in her banners.

All six children of her second marriage were to use the device by the end.

'It is most excellent wine of Gascony, my liege, and I will send four barrels as you have asked, to Rouen,' said the merchant loudly.

'Why did you not tell us there were goods for sale?' whined Countess Ela later on. 'The days are long here, and we women see nobody. I would have liked some wine.'

Later, he remembered that day as the commencement of the Franco–Scottish Alliance.

Matters hung fire regarding the coronation, it was rumoured because the Young King would have nobody but his old tutor Becket to crown him and the Old King would have any prelate other than the aforesaid. One way and another, the King of Scots and his brother David were bidden to London not for any coronation, but for Easter of 1170 to keep this with King Henry and his Court. It appeared that Henry himself had left Queen Eleanor behind at Caen with her daughter-in-law Marguerite and had himself crossed the Channel in a severe storm at the beginning of March, saying it was God's will whether he drowned or survived. One of his ships was lost, but he landed safe enough, and seemed prepared to play the friendly host. William, remembering Bellencombre, held himself ready for whatever might arise. He had told David a certain amount, but not everything: the young man had after all spent some years in England.

On Good Friday, he surveyed the bent heads of a mass of young folk, lacking only the Young King's French wife King Louis' daughter, detained across the seas with her mother-in-law and, they said, her coronation robes. Otherwise, with the tabernacle covered and the statues still veiled in their mourning purple, the bright heads of many stood out; the most flamboyant of Henry and Eleanor's family was young Richard, newly Count of Poitou, yellow of hair – they said he resembled his great-uncle Rufus, but was not yet as red in the face – and when he stood up for the long Gospel he was seen to be a full head taller than the handsome but effete young man about to be crowned, and broad of shoulder as well. William liked Richard of Poitou and they were already on friendly terms. Beside him, the smooth-mannered middle brother Geoffrey was nothing at all; William perceived the silver-fair head of little Constance of Brittany, the child Geoffrey was contracted to marry; she was here with her mother, William's own sister Margaret, who seemed to have grown remote; afterwards he could not remember whether her unlucky Conan was yet alive or dead, but was certainly very ill by then at Guincamp, while the Earl of Hereford, Henry's man, was already attentive to Duchess Margaret and, later, married her. Was that yet another of Henry's schemes? One could never be certain; but it seemed that everywhere there was an encircling power like an iron band, drawing inwards until everyone was caught up and imprisoned.

'The King is having all ports watched again, so that letters from the Pope may not come through forbidding any but Becket of Canterbury to carry out the crowning,' murmured David now. 'It will probably be done instead by old Roger, damn him.' Neither brother cared for Roger of Pont l'Evêque, Archbishop of York, the absent Becket's long enemy since youth and a man whose smug certainties made him disliked by both Scots. 'He said to me,' replied William angrily, 'that he not only has jurisdiction here in England, but over my bishops as well. I think I will not wait to see this crowning.'

He watched King Henry limp presently out of church; the energetic monarch had an ingrowing toenail which made him often lame, and besides had evidently not recovered from the voyage. What an act of Providence it would be if he were struck down after all! But no such thing happened; and William absented himself soon after the Easter ceremonies, as nothing had been said one way or the other about Huntingdon, let alone the purloined lands in the north. He made the excuse of Countess Ada's worsening health, and rode back without David; but paused on the way in London to visit a mistress there, whom he duly got with child. It proved later to be a son, and they called him Robert. William frequently sent word to enquire for Robert's progress, and money to ensure that he was adequately reared, as befitted a royal bastard; there were others by Henry, after all, though not as numerous as his royal grandfather's.

David remained not only for the Young King's coronation, which took place without that puppet's French wife, but waited on in England until Pentecost, when King Henry knighted him. By then, there was other news.

Six

Countess Ada stumped along on the arm of her messenger, Taurin de Bailleul, towards where the new Cistercian nunnery, meantime built of wood, stood nearby the rising stones of her projected abbey. It was December, and the King's mother wore her fur-lined cloak wrapped about her; being cold, so long as it stayed dry, was however less hard on the bones than pouring rain, and Ada's body ached less than usual. She was able to listen to the informed talk of de Bailleul, who had relations in Picardy and was also in touch, through her own habitual letters there, with Abbot Ailred's successor as well as with the Durham brotherhood. Ailred had died four years ago: one missed his gossip. De Bailleul was saying now that they were troubled about the safety of Archbishop Becket, who had lately returned to England despite all fears for his life.

'I cannot believe that even Henry would attack a consecrated Archbishop,' said Countess Ada. 'It is one thing to have ordered a mass for the dead to avoid having to give Becket the kiss of peace, but quite another – although my brother Reynald and others were most violent towards the Archbishop at Sandwich on his arrival lately after six years away – *quite* another thing to do him actual harm.'

She heard her own voice, the voice of a woman growing old: she felt in fact older than her age, old now and tired. Nevertheless the abbey was rising, the great Lamp of Lothian itself: it was Ada's daily pleasure to watch its progress, the placing of dressed stones, the dedicated carving of the craftsmen, not yet erected on pillars as would later happen. She brushed away the dust from her fur cloak; much was still drifting in the air, although the men did not of course work over Christmas, which was lately past. She thought of Reynald, whom she hardly knew now. His temper had not improved, she understood, despite the prosperous years at Poynton. He spent a good deal of his time away from Adelia, evidently, and sojourned instead about Court. 'He is no doubt angered,' she said aloud, for with Taurin she could speak her thoughts, 'by Archbishop Becket's having opposed the marriage of Isabel our niece to King Henry's young half-brother so that he died later of grief, and she had to make do with a bastard. I still cannot quite believe that reason for Prince William's death; how does one die of grief?' However they had said Queen Margaret Atheling did so, she remembered, hearing of the death of her husband King Malcolm in battle. 'At any rate, Reynald and the rest treated Becket in a way no consecrated churchman should be treated, cutting off the tail of his pack-horse and plundering his goods, even to taking the game in his forests for themselves. If Empress Maud had been alive she would have restrained her son King Henry in such ways: but since she died there seems nobody to whom he will listen, certainly not his wife.'

Taurin de Bailleul himself listened courteously, as was his way. It was not necessary to say anything; the old Countess was lonely, and liked to talk. He handed her presently into the nunnery, seeing her suitably received, and himself took a turn in the cold air till she should be ready again to come out. In this process, he saw a messenger riding in, his breath mingling with his horse's like a cloud in the cold air. The news came out of England. Becket had been murdered in his own cathedral at Canterbury the day after Christmas. By now, all the world knew.

'They say he called aloud on the Virgin and St. Alphège, who as you know was himself done to death in Queen Emma's time, when the Danes threw meat-bones at that good Archbishop until he was dead in his blood. Then at last the Archbishop now called on St. Benedict, and died. He could have saved himself, for there is a back stairway down which he could have escaped. Already, they are saying, miracles have happened at his tomb.'

'He was put into that promptly enough,' said the King, who had ridden down. 'They were coming back, the four murderers, to do the body further outrage, having meantime spilled its brains on the altar floor at sword-point.' Countess Ada shuddered. 'Becket however,' said the King, 'had given a good straight blow to William de Tracy in the old way when it started, but had no sword, being vested. They say he ended with the five wounds of Christ.' He spoke drily: he himself was not given to such comparisons.

'One of the murderers was our Constable's kin, alas; de

Morville, he who spilled the brains at last. When they entombed Becket and took off the rich robes, they found, next his skin, a hair shirt crawling with lice. He evidently mortified himself thus, in secret.' Countess Ada spoke without much conviction; she herself had never seen the point of such penances: they must be most uncomfortable and keep bringing themselves to mind at awkward moments. Meantime the King went to the window.

'As a martyr, Thomas Becket will be a greater danger to Henry than as the living troublemaker he was,' he remarked, looking out at the again busy workmen. 'Henry has put himself in the wrong in the eyes of all Christendom, whether or not he intended Becket to die. It may be his downfall.'

'That would please you. He was always your enemy.'

'Not that, perhaps, but tries to call himself my overlord. It will be a lighter task than before to prove him wrong.'

William's own mind was active. Henry II was still abroad. He would no doubt make pretence to interest himself in the affairs of Ireland to draw attention away meantime from himself, while Canterbury and the troubles with the Pope simmered on: the latter would, also without doubt, make a saint of Becket as soon as it was feasible. Such things nevertheless took time; meanwhile, he himself would consider the offer made four years ago now by King Louis, would consult his own lords – it was not advisable to imitate Malcolm's hasty actions made in his time without their approval – and would invade, with a strong force, the north of what was only lately a part of England, his own early province of Northumbria. It would happen soon, and with good will. Meantime, he awaited further word from France.

PART III

One

'It is true that Queen Eleanor has done her part for long enough in estranging the sons from their father, but the Young King has grievances; Henry kept him short of money, and also tried to take certain castles from him to provide a dowry for his favourite Lackland, whose marriage will not after all take place. That the Young King fled to his father-in-law Louis is understandable, if somewhat devilish for the Old; but when the Old's wife dressed herself up as a man and tried to follow her sons – the rest have gone also, or most of 'em – to the Court of her first husband whose daughter by a second marriage is one of the sons' wives, it makes Henry himself look ridiculous; and that is a thing he cannot endure. Fortunately for himself he captured Eleanor in time and she is now in prison. I wish I had seen her in her man's gear; they say she wore it in the old days with Louis on crusade, when she stole away to Saladin's tent and, they say, slept likewise with her uncle at Antioch. Now, such a woman will not be heard of again till Henry chooses to set her free. It will not be tomorrow.'

Ralph de Warenne, white-haired now and almost toothless, winked like the ancient satyr he probably was at the images arising in his mind. 'Close confinement! That's no different from the state Eleanor has been in since the marriage to Henry twenty years back. He used her as a brood-mare. Any woman of spirit would resent it, let alone one with great possessions.'

'They tell me the Young King's wife, Louis' daughter, has joined her husband in Paris,' Ada put in. Ralph winked again.

'Ask me rather what has happened to the other daughter, her sister Alais, who was supposed long since to be married to Richard, but they say his father King Henry visits her often enough in her chamber at Woodstock. Richard also is with the rest in Paris, naturally; he is not of a temper to endure that situation.'

The King of Scots listened, staring into his wine-cup. His

uncle was becoming garrulous, and delighted in nothing more than in spreading scandal up and down the country and, no doubt, across seas when he visited Normandy. For once, William himself had sympathy with Henry II. Increasingly as he resented the man, he respected his thoroughness as a ruler; and his sons were not of his calibre. One would sooner have him as an ally than those young men, or even Louis himself: the latter had been dilatory since the offer made that time four years since at Bellencombre. Few monarchs did anything in the end except to their own advantage; very well, it might be to his own to ignore Louis and bargain instead with the Old King. There could be, for instance, the return of Northumbria mooted in exchange for a promise to keep from invading the north of England oneself at a time of great embarrassment for Henry. One said nothing of that matter, naturally, in the presence of old Ralph; it would be all over the country too soon if so; but later he would discuss it with his mother, who would keep her counsel.

He was soon angry. Henry not only declined to bargain despite his known predicaments – they said he was contemplating a public penance for Becket's murder – but treated the offer with contempt. William therefore summoned a parliament of his nobles after Yule. The Young King aided by France, Leicester in the south, his own spearhead advancing from the north: they surely could not fail in such an enterprise.

My lords were, as always, ready for war against England; Malcolm the Maiden had made himself unpopular by too great a partiality for Henry at the beginning of his reign: his brother here was different. They rode south at last, with the lion banner flaring ahead in the wind; soon, it would become the symbol of Scotland. King William rode purposefully, his long legs gripping the mount's flanks with their stirrups: it was a colt he had trained himself, and obeyed him now swiftly and with affection between them, as should happen between a man and his horse. Behind the King followed a myriad coloured banners; the lion passant – everyone now adopted lions – of Gilchrist of Angus and his son Adam, riding now by him; Richard Comyn himself, Histilla's husband, and their sons, on the contrary with modestly flaunted golden sheaves, as if from fertile Slipperfield, now an Augustinian priory by their gift. Colban of Buchan, his austere face thoughtful beneath its still raised vizor – there was no danger yet – rode nearby the brothers from Galloway, Uchtred whom the King trusted and Gilbert whom he did not, with the latter's bastard son Malcolm, a rough lad who looked ready for anything; one must keep an eye on the Galloway men, they were out mostly for loot and gain for themselves, as in his grandfather's time at the Battle of the Standard. There was Alwin of Lennox, who had lately come to William from the west parts; and likewise – the King smiled to himself – young Morgun of Mar, who had suddenly appeared three years ago out of a forest and announced that he was the late mormaer's son. On investigation it had turned out to be true enough: it was probable that Morgun was also entitled to Moray, but one must wait till the end of this war. William de Haya was here, and magnificent Duncan himself, Earl of Fife, first of all the seven: Edgar of Dunbar also, with ten manors to regain in Northumbria in right of his wife; again, more lions rampant for Lindesay, called by somebody the greatest that the land had seen; but many today that rode were great. Nevertheless there were certain ones missing; Atholl, although his son Simon had come; the fierce black raven of Torphinn of Caithness was not among the banners, and one hoped that Torphinn would not elect to cause trouble in the far north now that the King's great army was riding down across the border; Strathearn likewise was absent, and Menteith, and the men of the Isles. The new Bishop Joscelin of Glasgow had however come, bearing a baton instead of a sword like his predecessor Odo of Bayeux at Hastings; his presence was cheering. Altogether it was a fair army. He, William, would lead it to victory: it was time. He spurred the beloved charger; the lion rampant flew out on the wind, the cold wind of his own soon-to-be-reclaimed Northumbria; by now, they had crossed the border. Presently they would lay siege to certain towns; David was already in France, supporting the Young King against his father. That young man had promised Westmoreland as well as Cambridge, and the debated lands. Westmoreland would grow fine corn, as fine as Lothian's. Scotland would again be great.

Two

Fool! Fool! Fool!

He repeated the word over and over to himself, striding up and down the confined space of the upper cell at Falaise. Falaise! At some time past, he had foreseen the word; Falaise, where Henry's ancestors had sewn leather at a trading-stall. Falaise, with its blackened stones unrelieved by tapestry in the December cold: a prisoner's place, made bleakly evident. He had been brought here by sea, with the rest. Before that they had taken him to Northampton, his earldom, with his feet tied beneath a horse; not *his* horse, that one was dead, in the field in the damned mist at Alnwick. Alnwick, where they had killed Ceann Mór. The mist, out of which they had blundered, the English army, not expecting to find him, the King of Scots, with the rest, taking their ease at a meal on the ground. The mist said now to be sent by Becket from heaven, on the very day Henry himself had knelt in penance at Canterbury and received three blows each from five prelates and eighty monks, after walking barefoot in penance in the mud. Henry must have had a sore back next day; but it had been a shrewd move, getting heaven on his side as well as, thereby, Europe and the Pope. Henry, a penitent. Himself, a prisoner. Alnwick. The mist, out of which they had come suddenly, and William, had left his meal on the summer grass and leapt instantly to horse; to the good trained colt, the beloved charger. Ranulf de Glanville had thrust a spear through its guts and they had spilled out, and the horse had rolled screaming and dying to the ground with him, the King of Scots, pinned helpless beneath its weight. Thus they had taken him, and bound him like a felon: and many knights, still fighting, had given up their freedom in order to ride with him to Northampton, then later to Richmond, then across seas for safer guarding, and now here. Here, he was left alone: in Falaise, the heart of Normandy. Falaise, where the

102

long-dead Conqueror had been born, having been got on a tanner's daughter Duke Robert had seen paddling in the river below here, and fancied for the time. A tanner stank and was never, however rich he might become, received into high company. William the Bastard, son of Robert the Devil. William the Conqueror. Henry, William's great-great-grandson, descended on his own side from the devil. Henry, the lately scourged penitent. Henry, his own gaoler. Henry could keep him, William the Lion, here for the rest of his life, unless he agreed to the vassalage of Scotland. Fool! Fool! Fool! A trifle of watching would have avoided capture. He had been too confident after success. Alnwick, the very place of ill omen where his own great-grandfather had been betrayed to death by his friend Morel of Bamborough. Alwnick, and now Falaise.

The horse. He had been fond of it. He had liked to watch it curvetting and playing, mane tossing, proud neck arched. Now, since July, it was a heap of stinking bones. How he had vaulted to the saddle, and plied his sword, and all done uselessly! A screaming dead weight rolling over and pinning him; then capture. Heavily guarded earlier, he was now left alone to reflect: the rest, he knew, were imprisoned somewhere in the fortress, even Leicester and his valiant countess, who had tried to drown herself at the English end rather than be taken prisoner. Countess Peronelle. She was of the breed of Eleanor of Aquitaine, and now both women were in prison. Henry, the provident, had conquered. Henry would make his own careful terms.

The Lion. If he, William, were ever to set foot in his own land again, if he were not to spend a lifetime in prison like blinded Robert Curthose at Devizes and Cardiff, learning Welsh to pass his days till he died, he must agree to the terms. He would abhor the oath; such an oath as had not even been extracted from his brother Malcolm in his time, for Malcolm had early piped to Henry's tune. An oath of disgrace, in exchange for freedom of a kind: that would be all, and he, the King, knew it.

He longed increasingly for a space beyond this cell, this town. He could see a little of the street from the window and the people who came and went. The Conqueror's obese ghost still hovered here at Falaise: he had rebuilt in his time the great fort, the huge keep out of which no man would ever win without leave. He, William, once and briefly called the Lion, could not pass his life here, striding forever up and down a blackened empty cell.

An oath extracted under force was not binding. Perhaps they would understand that, the rest. He must agree to take it; he had after all no choice. David his brother was in Henry's power as well. The Norsemen and the MacWilliams and the supposed descent of Lulach the Fool would overrun Scotland. He must take the oath of disgrace: and then, go home.

Henry II, recovered from his scourging and from the forced march of a hundred and fifty miles in two days he had made shortly beforehand in France, sat hard-eyed and smug now in his high chair; the King of Scots knelt before him. The terms were read out. They were humiliating, with King William's hands placed between King Henry's large neglected ones, feeling their warmth. Cold hands, warm heart. Warm hands, coldness of the ancestral devil. *I, William, am your liege man against every man in Scotland and all my other lands.* That clause about Scotland was new; it was evidently to be expected that the Scots themselves might rise. He had not met the glance of the other lords present; Fife, who had ridden gloriously down with him; Comyn, Colban, the rest. The Galloway brothers had made off at once from Alnwick and would be getting what they might from their grabbed freedom; he had heard on the voyage that they had already offered a large sum in silver to Henry if he would become their protector. Homage. Surrender of five castles, Edinburgh, Roxburgh, Berwick, Jedburgh, Stirling. Unable to marry without Henry's consent. He himself had not had leisure or inclination to think of marriage, but now that it was denied him, except on Henry's terms, resented the thought of it; he would be permitted, no doubt, to continue to take mistresses. More and still more of it: all the expressed attributes of shame. He rose presently, and saw Fife and the rest kneel in their turn and promise likewise. It was after all in nobody's interest to refuse now he, the King, had sworn. William found himself thinking, suddenly, of the old tale of Harold Godwinson and how he had been made to swear an oath by Duke William of Normandy on unseen saints' bones, disregarding it thereafter. Becket however had used his heavenly influence now, evidently, on behalf of the penitent Henry. Perhaps to build an abbey in Becket's honour somewhere in Scotland would be the answer, when he himself returned home. Would he be permitted to build such an abbey

by his overlord? One must ask, later. In the meantime,
dismissed by the complacent Angevin smile, they all, all the
Scots, filed out. In the silence that followed, nobody spoke.
Officially, he, William, was free to leave, to meet with the rest
later on and renew the oath under the smug gaze of Roger the
Archbishop, at York.

Three

'You could have done no other,' said Ada the Countess after William had returned.

She longed to comfort her angry and humiliated son, to take him in her arms as though he were her child again; but this man of thirty-three, with his face drawn and grim with the strain of the past year, seemed a stranger. He had told her, grinding out the words as though they hurt him, that on riding back at last towards his bartered kingdom his following, much depleted by then, had continued in silence; no man dared either look at the King or speak. As for the common people, they had hidden themselves, afraid no doubt of the revenge by pillage of a defeated army, or perhaps ashamed like the rest.

'Then there was York. That was the worst, almost worse than Falaise.' Again, at York, he had had to swear the damnable oath, by now involving his churchmen also, in the presence, again, of Roger of Pont l'Evêque, that same man who in life had been Becket's enemy; but there was no word of that now. *And all the bishops and abbots and clergy of the King of Scots and their successors shall do fealty to the lord King Henry as their liege lord, in the same way as the lord's other bishops are wont to do ... and the King of Scots, his brother and his barons, have granted ... that the Scottish church shall make submission to the English church as it ought to do, and as it was wont to do in the time of the lord king's predecessors...*

'That is not so,' said Ada. 'Christianity came to Scotland in the time of St. Ninian, a century or more before Augustine arrived in the south.' She remembered Earl Henry telling her of that, and of how he himself had made pilgrimage at times to Whithorn and the secret cave there, traversing with difficulty the long rough pebbled Galloway beach.

'Well, there will be no pilgrimages there for a while,' said William. 'Uchtred of Galloway and his brother have fallen out and made war as they always did, and Gilbert ended it by hacking Uchtred to pieces in his own house on Loch Fergus.

Gilbert offered Henry money then to save his own skin, likewise five hundred cattle and the like number of swine. Henry was not interested in the two last, and he declined the money because of Uchtred's murder.'

He scowled. He himself was prevented from marching, as he would have done, into Galloway at once to make war there against Gilbert, lacking Henry's permission; that would take its time about coming, no doubt. The position was intolerable: his lords had already made that evident. Never before had a King of Scots bowed to the English yoke; in MacBeth's time the latter had sworn to be King Cnut's man to aid him in war, but not as a vassal. There was an earlier tale about three kings in a boat, so long ago it was not worth considering; William's grandfather King David had fashioned a kingdom since.

Ada watched, aware that the tale of bloodshed in Galloway might well divert her son's mind from the similar horror of Falaise. Sooner or later he would be able, in some way, to become his own man again. Such a one as William the Lion would not remain the vassal for life of any other. Moreover, Henry of England would come to realise that if he bound William's freedom hand and foot in all such ways the country would become, once more, a mass of warring clanships without unity, cohesion, or even a name. Henry would surely not want such a situation on his northern borders. The future might well become clearer in such a way than the present. Meantime, it remained to be seen what the Scots bishops would say to the attempt to purloin their independence; there could always be an appeal made to the Pope.

Meantime, there were stirrings in the north and west, as there had been when Ada herself, newly widowed, had had to rule for a child of twelve till Malcolm grew to manhood. 'We had thought this King now was a man,' they were saying everywhere bitterly.

Gilbert of Galloway, the murderer, had already during the year's imprisonment expelled William's officers and razed his castles, as though the province were a kingdom to itself; for generations, after all, it had behaved like one when it could. The King sent word to his self-appointed overlord, who as expected took his time about replying. When he did so, it was merely to reprimand Gilbert of Galloway and cause him to pay a fine. Gilbert retaliated by promising death to any of his own underlings who swore fealty to the King of Scots.

One thing presently cheered the King; the appearance of a young lad with honest eyes, who knelt to him. This was Roland of Galloway, son of the murdered Uchtred. 'My father was loyal to you,' he said. 'I will not avenge him. It is time there was peace in the region.'

He spoke shyly; it was probable that he had culled his notions from his mother Gunnhild, who had been a niece of old Gospatric of Dunbar, King David's friend who had fallen long ago before the Standard. 'I am your man,' Roland promised William now. The King raised him in his strong grasp.

'Stay by me if you will,' he told the boy. 'It is possible that I may ride soon to the north, and would be glad both of your aid and –' he smiled for the first time – 'your company.'

'I will come. I know well enough now to wield a sword. The King of England's writ will not run in the far north; even he cannot get there. I must return now to my father's poor folk, for my uncle will be hard on them. He will not prevail, never fear.' The young mouth was set in determination.

William let the boy go, saying he would be glad to see him again in Ross and Moray. He had determined not to wait, this time, for Henry's leisure to reply. Worse could befall in Moray and Ross by way of claimants there who were left free to decide for themselves in those remote parts, and were vassals to no man; and he would say so if needed.

Next year, he had so far prevailed as to bring the murderer Gilbert to York to meet with Henry himself. Henry seemed unchanged, outwardly amiable now he had what he wanted, or thought so. Gilbert of Galloway's young son Duncan, a lad with a shifty glance, was left with the English King as hostage; and for the time there was, accordingly, peace in the west. It would be ten years before Roland of Galloway defeated his uncle's men in a furious fight, no doubt using the experience he had gained lately with the King in Moray; and by the end, when he could do so, William created his faithful adherent Lord of Carrick, the north half of the province. More could not be done at that time.

He had ridden down to Northampton meantime in a bitter January, in company with the grim-mouthed Scots bishops. They had already made up their minds. Roger and his clerics greeted them at last with the show of heartiness the Archbishop always made when he thought he had won. *And all the bishops and abbots and the clergy of the King of Scots shall do fealty ...*

He made smooth mention, at an early stage, of the clause that Scotland would be placed under an interdict if the King defaulted from his treaty with Henry. The clause was an extension of the arrogance shown at Clarendon against which Becket had held out and in the end, had paid for with his life. William decided that there was maybe a martyr of similar fibre in the presence of Gilbert, Bishop of Moray, who would hardly suffer himself, cold as he was from the ride, to swallow the Archbishop's warm mulled ale. There was still little talk from the Scots, but much from Archbishop Roger. He was a man who respected birth, which had been one reason for his treatment of Becket, recalling the latter's humble origins. That such a man should have succeeded above himself had caused envy to eat into Roger of Pont l'Evêque all his life. Now, he talked down to the King of Scots, who wished him at the devil.

They met in session, and the demand was formally repeated that obedience to England should be enforced from the church in Scotland as well as from her King. Bishop Wishart of Glasgow rose first; his mitre might have been a helm.

'As we ought to do, you say? As we were wont to give? When was that? We have never given anything to your folk save a shared charity as Christians, which thing we were long before yourselves.'

The Archbishop interposed, the expression on his face having modified itself to express a mild amusement. 'The Holy Father himself, in the time of this King's late brother, whose soul God rest, outlined that situation clearly enough. There is no doubt concerning it.'

'The Pope for the time was Nicholas Breakspear, a damned Englishman; and even so he did not succeed in his claims, as well ye know.'

The Bishop of Moray was on his feet by now, his face bright with anger; he was said to glow like hot iron when roused. 'The Church in Scotland was founded long before your own,' he continued. 'It is your mother. The blessed Columba died in the very year your Augustine – who converted Kent, granted, but never Wales – was consecrated bishop. Columba had lived long and journeyed far, preaching the Gospel when you in England were still pagans and slaves. The blessed Ninian was earlier still, and founded his church in Candida Casa, which is our

Whithorn in case you know it not, in the fourth century, before the Roman legions had marched out of your country, for they never conquered ours.'

There was murmuring among the listeners, and Roger of York, not losing his pleasure in himself for that he could never do, leaned over and playfully smacked the Bishop of Moray's head. The Scots uprose then, and there would have been turmoil had not some of the English present, themselves in agreement and also remembering the trouble there had been in Rome about violence to Becket, calmed everyone down. Almost everybody had been shouting except the Lion, who sat silent in his place. He was proud of Wishart and of Moray. Their courage in a foreign land made him ashamed of his own weakness. He should have stayed at Falaise, a prisoner, and said his prayers for the rest of his life. At all events Henry could hardly detain the entire Scots hierarchy in Northampton; some at any rate must be allowed to ride home.

This happened, with remarks however to the effect that the Bishop of Moray was a vapouring and headlong Scot. As the Pope was no longer an Englishman but an Italian, it was decided that the matter had best be referred to him after all.

A thing happened then which made King William, when he was informed at last, realise to what depths Henry and his Archbishop Roger, who must have known of it, would sink to obtain their will. A letter was evidently sent to the Pope as if from himself, and signed with his seal. It stated that he had certainly wished the fathers of the church to conform and swear fealty to Henry. A copy – copies had been circulated among his bishops – was shown to him at last by the Archbishop of St. Andrews. William heard it read aloud and presently thundered out his chosen oath.

'By the arm of St. James, I sent no such letter.'

The Archbishop inclined his head. 'We thought not, my liege. This will need careful answer. That the Holy Father may be aware of such a likelihood is proven by the fact that he sent copies back to us. It will be the best thing, if this can be achieved, to have a Papal legate sent to Scotland, in order that this may be discussed face to face.'

'Would this be better than sending a Scots delegation to Rome?'

'Ay. Such a delegation might be prevented by Henry from ever reaching the Holy City. It is less likely – though a legation will certainly have to travel through England – that he will detain a Papal representative and all his train, at least for long.'

William, wrenching himself out of his habitual bitter thoughts, remembered that the foundations of a great abbey were being laid now at Arbroath. It should be dedicated, he had decided, to the Honour of God, the Blessed Virgin and – he gave a wry inner acknowledgement – to St. Thomas Becket, the man so greatly disliked by Roger of York. Rumours of the canonisation of the Canterbury martyr were rife already, and there had been further miracles at Thomas's tomb.

As an officially penitent and well-scourged sinner, Henry II, although he had certainly, as expected, detained the Pope's legates when they were sent without too much delay, did not take it upon himself to refuse, at last, the keys of the castle of Edinburgh for the parley itself. A scarlet-clad procession, surrounding the Legate, Cardinal Viviani, in his great tasselled hat, and followed by the Scots hierarchy solemnly vested, rode upwards on mules to the lowered portcullis and entered in. The gaping citizens were left meantime in ignorance of what was being decided, and so was the King. William spent the day in deep dejection, assuming that all would go against him as by custom now; there had been an affray lately in the north when certain leaders refused to proceed under him, while the rest refused, on the contrary, to fight unless he stayed. Such were the conditions under which he now laboured, and his mother had not long to live. The bishops' courageous stand at Northampton might well come to nothing; men such as Roger of York would always prevail. For a man not to move hand or foot in defence of his own realm without asking permission was shame enough; one supposed it was worse to have jurisdiction from the south about one's very soul.

He went to Malcolm's prie-dieu, which his dead brother had used somewhat oftener than himself; and knelt down before the crucifix. He had a good confessor, Hugh, who knew like William himself that William's chief abiding sin was lechery. Even his mistresses seemed less compliant than before, or so he had lately decided; today, he did not even feel like thinking of women.

He rose from his knees, without much good done upon them, and began to walk up and down the room as he had walked at Falaise three years since. However here there was the rustle of fresh straw he had had put down for the visit the Legate would almost certainly make him, later, whichever way the verdict had gone; not to do so would be discourteous, and this new Pope Alexander had, so far, shown courtesy even in the lack of delay. He himself must shed the black dog from his shoulder in time to become a pleasant host. They could converse, he and the Legate, in Latin; he had been well enough taught in youth at least to the degree needed to understand his own charters. Henry, damn his eyes, would dictate the latter now.

Falaise! Falaise! He, William, had never been his own man since.

Footsteps came, and with them the familiar face of Hugh with good news, culled early. 'My liege' – they still used the accustomed address, at least – 'it is most excellent. His Holiness has confirmed the rights of the Scottish Church to its own rule, subject only to himself. He has sent instructions that no homage is to be paid to the King of England by us, nor are we beholden to any of his clergy. That cheers you, does it not?'

It was a triumph. William felt a great lifting of his spirits. He was able to entertain Cardinal Viviani presently with dignity and good wine, aware always of the compassionate shrewdness in the Italian's eyes. Before he left, Cardinal Viviani related in a low voice what had happened during their journey through England.

'The King there sent to me two bishops on our landing; the Bishop of Winchester and the Bishop of Ely. Their purpose – ' he smiled, and toyed with his wine-cup for moments – 'was to enquire by whose permission we had landed.'

'It does not sound as if he has taken Becket's martyrdom greatly to heart; he might have said as much in the days of Clarendon.'

'Indeed, and we were told at first that unless we were ready to abide by the will of the King of England we would not be allowed to proceed further.'

'That was impertinence,' said William angrily. 'How did you evade it? Henry is a stiff-necked man, and less clever than he thinks himself. It would be folly thus to make an enemy of His Holiness, as by now even he should know.'

'Sire, I am a diplomat. I made pretence to be fearful, which flattered them. I was then made to swear on the word of truth that I would do nothing on the legation hostile to King Henry or his kingdom. As his kingdom is of this world and not the next, I could swear this in all conscience.' The dark eyes twinkled. 'We were suffered then to depart. In fact he gave us letters of protection, and an escort, and the abbots and English bishops were instructed to receive me with the honour due to a cardinal.'

'He could hardly do less,' growled William. 'Your Eminence is one.' It explained the ease with which the castle keys had been delivered. Even Henry would not put himself in the wrong again so soon in the eyes of Europe.

Four

Ada the Countess sat in the sun at Haddington, in the garden made over the years by her endowed Cistercian nuns. She often had herself carried here for the peace to be found among the growing things, watching the quiet figures of the white-robed sisters moving, tending the herbs and parsley. There were times when Ada wondered if she were hypocritical in having founded, during her sons' two reigns, more women's religious houses in Scotland than ever before, when she herself had never left the world or thought of so doing, and even somewhat resented Cistercian thought itself, which had given rise to Malcolm's unnatural vow. She herself was no nun: she looked back on her marriage with happiness, fulfilment, and regret that it had been cut short so early. It was for those reasons that she had remained a faithful widow to Earl Henry now for twice as long as the years of their companionship together as husband and wife.

She sighed a little, remembering also her dead son the Maiden King. It was because of her own recalled happiness in such matters that she had tried to put a little in Malcolm's way; possibly it had been wrong of her. The child, in any event, had died. By now, the recollection of Malcolm himself and Earl Henry had blurred together in her mind, one figure only remaining, an angel's with bright hair. No doubt both Malcolm and his father were at one with God. There had been prayers said for them up and down the land, at the time of the deaths and since. How long would it be before she, an old woman now, might be permitted to follow?

There were so many dead. Ralph her brother was no longer alive to visit her and bring her the gossip of the great world; lacking his visits, she was beginning to be remote from almost everyone except her sons. The King, and his brother David, had troubles of their own. Both were Normans, like herself. She smiled. There had been no need to ply either son with wine any more to induce the taking by them of young women; David already had two bastard sons, both named for his father. William, poor William, had become sombre of late years; he did not neglect his own earlier conceived bastard children, but seemed more greatly taken up nowadays with the building of his abbey at Arbroath, which he and others had enriched greatly with lands. The faded Brecbennoch, the banner of Columba himself, was among the treasures; William had told her of that last time he came. It had been borne in front of the great saint himself when he visited St. Kentigern at Glasgow, a green place on the Clyde.

William. William Garbh, the brawny one. She wished she could see him settled and made happy, with a wife of his own. He had joined a Benedictine fraternity at Arbroath, though not – Ada smiled again to herself – now or ever as a monk; it was strange to think of the black cloak enveloping the Lion's burly and contentious body. The unpopularity with which he had been greeted in Scotland on return from Falaise was dying down; it was gradually being realised, as she had said to him at the time, that he could have done no other than submit. At least he had been returned to her instead of being held forever in prison in Normandy: it was almost four years now. He looked an older man than he was by far: she was troubled for him. A monarch of William's age should be making heirs to the throne. 'King Henry greatly resented Margaret's and Ada's marriages abroad,' their mother reminded herself. 'He thought it gave us too much power overseas.' The marriages still seemed as if they had happened yesterday; yet both her daughters had growing children by now, with Constance married long ago to King Henry's son Geoffrey. One seldom heard from Brittany, though sometimes the pair came across to Richmond in Yorkshire, for the hawking to be had on the moors there, but she herself never now ventured south for any reason, even that.

She moved her stoutening body a little, feeling her breaths shorten as they often did nowadays. Beyond the garden was her own town of Haddington, prosperous and busy, with its market selling produce from the rich surrounding fields of Lothian; it had been a good place to build both town and abbey. The Lamp itself was not yet finished: such enterprises could not be hastened. She herself would never now see it completed and knew as much. She, Ada de Warenne, a Norman of the old race, mother of a line of kings, could die when God willed, her duty done.

She felt discomfort then, a very little; and saw a man's bright-haired figure standing in the garden. He wore white raiment. Had there not been some tale of a clerk who had a vision of Malcolm, clad so? But this was not Malcolm, surely, but her husband, Earl Henry himself. The two had always resembled one another. It did not seem strange to Ada that her husband should be here now: he had come for her. He stood waiting in the sunlight, and she felt herself rise and go to him, a young girl again, leaving her body behind.

'Come, Ada,' he said. 'You have done well. Take my hand. It is not far.'

Shortly a nun, passing by, saw that the Countess was dead. She did not break the Cistercian silence, but went quietly in to tell her Prioress, who sent for the chaplain. They would arrange presently for the great bell to ring over the town of Haddington and thus convey the news to the King, in Edinburgh.

Five

'We have licence, at least, to build two castles. It is not likely our overlord will ever set eyes on them.'

'To hell with him,' said David the King's brother, riding beside William. 'The Conqueror himself did not dare come further north than Abernethy. We are many miles further on now than that. Place your forts where you desire them.'

The King grunted. He had become increasingly taciturn since their mother's death last year: but thereafter the two brothers had grown ever closer. They were much of a kind, big Normans, with the same habit of taking what they wanted but then using it responsibly. David was less troubled with black moods than the King, having less reason.

Nevertheless the Lion banner waved again, with an army behind it and, this time, no dissension among the lesser leaders; possibly Prince David's presence reassured them now he had returned from France. The force had already travelled and fought all over the mountain country between east and west, here in remote Ross; Sgurr Mór, Sgurr Bán, Sgurr Ruadh; flushing out pockets of rebels and putting paid to them in the accepted fashion, but without yet capturing the elusive Donald Bán MacWilliam, father by now of sons and a daughter profitably married. It had seemed best to the King – Henry's permission had been graciously forthcoming – to fortify two places, one on either coast, by the Dornoch Firth and conversely, across a narrow passage to the very island of Skye itself. The latter fort would keep watch for Norse invaders if they came that way: it had happened before and would no doubt happen again.

William began to feel his own man once more in this wild country, with the great arms of sea-lochs thrusting inland and the frowning mountains reflected above the sea. They would change colour, he knew already, from the hue of the heather itself to the dulness of iron or, again, the blue-grey of

117

pervading mist. The Gael in him – the blood of Ceann Mór ran far back – called out to the people here and had gained, to a certain extent, their loyalty when they set eyes on him. England to them was a place very far away: what they resented was the coming of the Norman. They had not all even seen for themselves this Donald Bán MacWilliam who, though admittedly a bastard, claimed by descent from Malcolm III and Ingebjorg to be the true King of Scots. This present King, whom men called the Lion, with his grim set face and tall body clad in mail, was a warrior and no monk, and had moreover been anointed at Scone years since. Thus they respected him, and knelt, as much to William meantime as to the great red-and-gold lion banner, which was new. In time to come there would be loyalty among them to the Lion itself, while kings came and went or else were lacking: but not yet.

The brothers separated shortly, one to see to the building of one great fort and one the other. The stones rose faster in each than at Arbroath, where the building was still being completed with care and craftsmanship; here, the main necessity was strength. Garrisons of sworn men were placed there, then the King and his brother rode back, having extracted the promise that swift word would be sent across the hills if trouble should arise. Then King William rode back towards the southern parts of his kingdom, those that no longer welcomed him as greatly as here; though there had been sympathy for him in Lothian over the death of his mother, it had been partly lost again by William's new quarrel with, of all persons, the Pope.

It had arisen over the preference he himself had for his confessor Hugh, whom he wanted made Archbishop of St. Andrews in preference to one John; the man deserved it. He, William, had been a trifle high-handed, which he knew even then was foolish, his temper having grown short nowadays with provoking events. Pope Alexander had been Scotland's friend, and to act, on his own account, as Henry however had himself done over Becket in the early days was to risk trouble at Rome. It came, in the form of excommunication and the placing of a final decision by means of, of all men, Roger of York. 'He turns up like a bad coin,' grumbled David. Discontent festered again in Lothian; first this King had submitted to England, and now had got them into a position where no sacraments could be administered except for baptism and burial. William was glad that his ally, young Roland of Galloway, had married his de

Morville bride in time; it was a love-match, and Helen gave birth within the year to a son and named him Alan. Her young husband had more success yet in his province's war, which still raged there, once his unpleasant murderous uncle Gilbert was dead. Roland took the bit between his teeth and raised his own army despite King Henry, swearing to lay tree-trunks in the way of any advancing English force. King William however persuaded the young fire-eater meantime to submit. 'I will requite you when I may,' he promised, already thinking of the prospect for Roland of the lordship of Carrick.

There were three convenient deaths then. Old Louis VII of France expired at last, to be succeeded by his son Philip. The Pope also died. William regretted the ill-feeling there had lately been with the Pontiff who had shown kindness towards Scotland; he hastened to establish friendship with the new Pope Lucius III. Matters were settled by a third vacancy occurring, that of the see of Dunkeld; like a game of chess, the choice of the late Pope and Roger was transferred here, Hugh the Confessor gained St. Andrews after all, and presently, with the great final roofing of the Abbey of Arbroath, a gift was sent to King William which conveyed great favour from the Lateran; the Golden Rose itself. It was more than English Henry had ever received, or would. It was brought by as solemn a legation as had wound in its day up to Edinburgh Castle, and William received it with dignity and gratitude. It raised his prestige, as he knew, not only abroad, but in the eyes of his own people.

After the ceremony, he knelt alone for a time before the Rose. It was not the grandest or the most beautiful thing he had ever seen; carved images and reliquaries, the Black Rood of Scotland his great-grandmother had brought, the matchless jewels on St. Thomas's tomb at Canterbury, said to be finer than anything in the world, would rival it, no doubt; but it was an honour to have received it. The goldsmith's work was fine, with tiny sapphires at the heart of each lesser rose, the main stem holding a large gold blossom and a receptacle for pouring in balsam and sweet spices. Beauty and sweetness had been foreign to William for a long time; the gift was welcome. He said a prayer for the lack of success of the present antipope Pascal: one must support one's friends. If only his mother could have been alive to know of the honour of the Rose! Perhaps she knew, where she had gone, that he had received it. He must keep guard on his temper, that was all; as David said, there was no call to imitate Henry Plantagenet and chew straw whenever one felt ill-disposed. He himself must bide his time quietly now; Henry was growing older; but, granted, so was he. In a year's time he would be forty. It was time he married; perhaps, now that the Pope was his ally, Henry would permit him a suitable bride, then David also might agree to marry in time. They had after all begun to do most things together. William gazed at the sapphires in the Golden Rose, reflecting and planning. He would ride again south, but not yet.

As if in benign approval of the entire state of affairs, Henry restored to him, three years later, the Earldom of Huntingdon. There were bound to be reasons, and one was the death of the Young King, of fever, in 1183. William made his preparations to ride into England and, meantime, enfeoffed his brother with the title. David Earl of Huntingdon had by now fathered his two bastard sons, both named Henry. It was time that the King and his brother took wives unto themselves, and fashioned true heirs to the Crown.

Six

The King of Scots had not ridden out that day with the King of England's hunt, though he had been with it down here most days since the start of the season. The familiar black dog was on his shoulder again, and he strode off alone, hearing with resentment the winding of horns die out in the distance beyond Woodstock.

There was no particular reason for his mood today; King Henry had as usual now been hospitable, exercising his charm as a host to the full, perhaps in excess. He, William of Scotland, was forty-four, and beginning to feel as if he had made a fool of himself all his life. David, who might have heartened him with his company, was elsewhere; their mother was eight years dead, his own bastard children scattered, some married. He must ride soon across from here to London to see the boy Robert, now well grown. His casual mistresses meant little now, less even than some had briefly meant; he recalled his long-ago passion for Avenel's daughter as if it had happened to some other man. On the whole, he was fondest of his daughters, particularly Isabel whom his mother had loved. Isabel was by now the wife of de Brus of Annandale, grandson of his grandfather's mentor at the Standard who had at the time vainly begged King David not to fight. Ada, called after his mother, was newly Countess of Dunbar; there was a Margaret, and there was, lastly, Africa. He reflected on his youngest daughter's name. She had been called, for it was the fashion, after the strange new continent that had become manifest with the Crusades, and which was only as yet known at its outermost shores, no one having penetrated the dark inner mysteries said to lie beyond: rivers, deserts, unknown mountains peopled by savage tribes; in its way – he smiled grimly – it sounded like Moray.

He, its King, had betrayed his kingdom. Everything came back to that no matter how one's thoughts edged away, for the time. He had sold Scotland, and himself, to Henry, his

121

over-courteous host here at Woodstock, where Queen Eleanor, one's fellow-captive in that man's toils, had at last, after many years, been freed after a fashion, to savour the company of her daughter Matilda, Duchess of Saxony, who was at Court with her exiled husband Henry the Lion. Henry the Lion and William the Lion, both under one set of painted Woodstock ceilings. There had been a third Lion also, long dead; the first husband of Henry's late mother, the Empress Maud. Maud, Beauclerc's daughter, the Empress at twelve years old when her first husband was, if one remembered correctly, fifty-four. It had nevertheless been a happy marriage; the second, with Geoffrey Plantagenet, had not been. This Lion of Saxony now said little enough of how he had been ejected under the new Emperor's ban; the talk at the high table remained courteous like their host these days, and general. However the German Duke had once ruled all lands from the Baltic to the Mediterranean; it must be humiliating to be here, a pensioner of one's father-in-law.

His wife Matilda however sparkled; she was a taking creature, perhaps like her mother Eleanor had been permitted to be in youth in Provence. Younger than her husband, Matilda of Saxony seemed to make even her mother carefree again by her presence; there was laughter at Court for the first time in long. As a rule, conditions here were strict, in their way.

William strode on down the deserted grass paths, seeing now and again the straggling Provençal roses Queen Eleanor had caused to be planted in the old palace gardens years since, during her frequent childbearings. Thereafter, with her imprisonment, they had become neglected. William himself knew little about flowers: there had been no time. His mother might have known, in her Cistercian garden.

Ada the Countess. He, her son, missed her more than he could say. As a rule a woman given power – witness Queen Eleanor herself and to what it had brought her – could become a troublesome force, an enemy to a strong husband; such women were perhaps better made abbesses. Poor Mary of Boulogne, having petitioned the Pope accordingly, was long ago back in her convent at Romsey, having resumed her duties there; such a return could not have been easy. The two children, by now almost grown, were in charge of their father and the King. Children. The ancient curse. William sometimes remembered it, as now, walking and walking alone. Henry's son, the Young King, was dead also, of a fever. It accounted for

William's own better treatment. Now, there were the pleasances and the plantings, and he cared nothing; servitors came and went to make ready the great hall for the return, later on, of the hunt, and he watched them idly. There would be slaughtered deer tied by the feet, borne in on poles, the blood congealing where their guts had been torn out at the kill. For once, he had not cared to watch it happen.

There was a very young girl playing now by herself on the grass, tossing and catching a ball made of sewn leather. Her movements were graceful and she seemed content with her own company; her mouth smiled. William stared; the child's long flying hair, the very manner of turning her slender body, reminded him of something and someone, a memory of long ago: his young sister Matilda, of whom he had been fond; the one who had been born at first without hair or fingernails. She would have grown to become a pretty graceful creature such as this, instead of having ailed and died, in the same year as their father. Had she lived longer, she might have been like this girl, hair confined by a fillet across the white young brow, small breasts beginning to show provocatively beneath the loose light summer robe. William called out, with a kind of compulsion, in the French they all used, her name.

'Mathilde.'

She stopped her game of tossing and spun round, the leather ball held in both hands. Her smile widened to laughter, and she answered in a voice which was not that of the English Court; she was evidently a foreigner, her French having broad vowels, like his own.

'How is it, Freiherr, that you my wrong name know? They call me that here because everyone in the family is Matilda unless they know better. My name is Richenza, after my uncle the Count of Poitou.'

He knew then who she was: Henry the Lion's daughter, grandchild of the King of England himself. She had been kept apart from the rest at Court, no doubt with her mother among the Queen's women. William stumbled out some reply.

'Do not trouble about it,' said the child placidly, and came to him and held out her hand. 'I am of the ball game tired. There many Matildas were, grandmothers and cousins and aunts, also my mother. Let us go to look at the great maze; come with me.'

She seemed to trust him, though like any man he could take her in the dark corners of the maze by force, abusing her innocence. He began to feel like her protector, almost her father; God knew he was old enough. He let Richenza of Saxony lead him into the twisting shadowed mysteries of the close-clipped yew. The maze was older even than King Beauclerc's time, possibly even than the Confessor's. They wound through it together, the young girl seeming familiar with its secrets. No doubt she had used her solitary hours to find her way in and out of it: at Woodstock, the King's granddaughter would be considered safe.

As they went Richenza chattered, seeming glad of someone to whom to talk. 'I will show you the place to which we now come,' she said. She turned her head mischievously, laughing again, and he could see her little white teeth, a kitten's. 'This place is most secret; only my grandfather knew. I must lead you, therefore, or you will be lost and they will find you in years to come, a *knockengerlüst*, a skeleton. Come and see.'

At the end, after avoiding many blind alleys, they came to a pavilion. Unlike the King's meticulous care of everything of the kind it had become neglected, its paint long left to peel; it had once been green in colour, with decorated panels of flowers, mostly roses. Richenza sat down on the bench inside and swept away the dust and leaves, patting it so that William might join her. She treated him, and had from the beginning, as someone of her own age, a boy. If only he were William Garbh again! The thought itself cheered him and he felt less lonely in her company. He sat where he could watch her face. It still had a look of his little dead sister. This was, when one considered it, not surprising; there had been so many marriages between England and overseas, with the Conqueror's line and that of Matilda of Flanders, and Stephen's wife's Boulogne kin, and the Athelings, that everyone was related. Richenza even resembled, a very little, his own niece Constance of Brittany as he had heard her described, silver-fair, still, a proud beauty.

'My grandsire the King told me, but he said to tell nobody, that he used to come here to visit a very beautiful lady named Rosamund, but she is dead,' the child said. 'I have told nobody but you, and you must tell no one else: promise me.'

'I promise.' He had heard of Rosamund Clifford, who had borne the King two sons; she was dead now, in a tomb at Godstow nunnery. Henry, then, could love. So could he. He could love this child, could marry and cherish her. There was less of a difference in age than there had been between the King's mother and the first husband who had made her happy: he had lately been thinking of them both.

He found himself fondling the child's hand, which she had left in his. 'Are you happy here in England?' he asked her. 'Would you perhaps like to see my country? It is in the north, and cold.' His voice sounded brusque in his own ears. Richenza of Saxony smiled.

'It is cold in my country also, when the wind blows off the sea,' she said. 'When we are at Lübeck, my father's town, my mother wears her furs. I like Lübeck greatly; there are images of St. Anne with a little Virgin in her lap, and in the Virgin's lap a tiny Christ. I have not seen that in your country.'

'England is not my country. If you will come to Scotland, you shall have images of St. Anne, as many as you choose; and anything else you may desire.'

'Perhaps, then,' she said, suddenly prim, and rose. 'I must go back now.' They went back, still with hands clasped to show William the way, through the dark maze and out into the August sunlight, where one of the Duchess of Saxony's waiting-women was already looking for her charge. William noted the quick expression of alarm in the servant's eyes as she perceived the young girl come out of the maze with the *farouche* middle-aged King of Scots, who was known to take women as he pleased and bowl them over like ninepins; but from the look of things the Lady Richenza had taken no harm.

When Henry returned from the hunt William waited until he should have washed himself clean of blood. Then he went to him with a request to marry his granddaughter. Henry stared for instants with his hard light eyes, then burst out laughing in the way he had and slapped his fellow-monarch on the shoulder.

'It may be,' he said. 'God willing, the matter will go well.' His gaze scanned William not unkindly, seeing a big man with greying hair and, today at least, the eyes of a hesitant boy. It was politic at the moment to keep the King of Scots contented: there was trouble on most other fronts. 'The Pope must, of course, be consulted,' he added. 'With his consent, the matter shall be concluded most gladly.'

He had, as was his way, not troubled to consult the girl's parents: both were his dependants for the time. The marriage of William of Scotland was in his gift as overlord, and it was time: if it could not be this girl, it should be another. He would keep the matter in mind.

Seven

'You are reading from the *Peregrenatio Silviae*; the name is mistaken. I myself have been in Syria, and the name of the lady concerned was Eucheria; she came from northern Spain, and travelled a thousand miles, God knows how. She stood at last on the shores of the Red Sea, and on Mount Sinai, where the monks showed her many things.'

Queen Eleanor's low-pitched voice had interrupted the reader, a young woman not notable but who read well. She raised wise eyes now from the book till the Queen had finished instructing the company. It included, for the rain was pattering down outside, not only Duchess Matilda and her young daughter, but other ladies and some men. Among these was the King of Scots, known by everyone at Court to be besotted with young Richenza. His eyes sought her out now and she gave him a quick confiding smile. Some of the women, including the Duchess her mother, were busy with embroidery, but Queen Eleanor herself disliked this pursuit; she preferred to listen to informed reading or else to write songs and sing them in the *langue d'oc*, the tongue of yea and nay: even in this place of Woodstock where her lord the King had kept her long under close surveillance, or else at Winchester. It was easier since their daughter Matilda had returned for the time from Germany: one hoped the Emperor would not relent too soon. How awkward the great big-boned King of Scots looked, standing idle by the door-curtain, gazing at little Richenza as if she were a sweetmeat! Eleanor of Aquitaine knew, as she knew most things that went on in her husband's mind, that Henry had no real intention of allowing such a marriage; it was doubtful if he had even troubled to send word to the Pope.

William turned his eyes from Richenza – he must not shame her by staring always – to look at Eleanor herself as all men still did, although the Queen was sixty-four years old and her fabled beauty had somewhat dried and shrunken. Its remains

126

could still be seen in the high cheekbones and oblique languorous eyes, the long hands and closed ironic smile. Despite everything that had happened to her, life still amused the Queen of England. 'Read to us again, Ermengarde,' she said.

William took little heed of the reader, although her quiet voice was restful. His gaze had shifted again to Richenza, caused by her mother meantime to tidy the skeins of coloured silk they were employed with in some manner. It occurred to him that he had not again been permitted to be alone with her; perhaps that was not to be expected. When he got her with him to Edinburgh, he would be careful of her; she was too young to bear children yet; she would be a plaything, a pleasure, for a year or two. He could hardly wait to win her. In himself he was a young man again. He tried to listen to the rest of the tale of the travels of Lady Eucheria, how the good monks had shown her the places where Moses and Aaron had stood and King David had passed by; then the place of the agony of Christ, the Rock of Gethsemane, the other little rock of the Ascension, the brook Kedron itself, and the Column of the Flagelltation which the monks kept now carefully on Mount Sion. Queen Eleanor raised her head in its broad gold circlet and veil.

'The scourging was by no means on Mount Sion, but a few paces only from the house of Pilate; my uncle told me of that in Antioch. Saint Petronius went to Jerusalem in the fifth century with a measuring rod, and came back to build seven churches in Bologna exactly as the Holy Places had been.'

'Men would have heard from their grandfathers of it, and they in turn from theirs,' said Matilda of Saxony. 'Such things are not forgotten. The gift of the Vernacle, the Sacred Face on St. Veronica's handkerchief, occurred five hundred paces from the house of Pilate. I heard of that in Germany.'

'It was a grievous way to travel,' remarked the reader quietly.

Queen Eleanor shrugged; she was herself more pagan than Christian. 'Let us have music now,' she demanded, and when the notes she loved, which to William's thinking were always a trifle discordant, began to sound, he made his bow of courtesy and took himself off. The sooner he was married, and away from all this, with Richenza, the more at home he would feel. He longed for Scotland, with its sharp air, in this place where even the rain was warm as it fell. He had had word again, also, of stirrings in those two places which forever caused trouble, Moray and Galloway. He must sound the King to hasten the decision of the Pope.

Henry was evasive. In the end it transpired that he had made, or said he had, enquiries, 'but it is of no value, my friend, to pursue the matter; in fact, as we discovered, the child herself is your niece.' He gave his boisterous laugh. William felt the blood go back to his heart. Folly, more folly! He should have known: now, they all knew, and would mock.

'How can this be?' he heard himself ask. He was told a farrago of some sort involving his eldest sister Ada and her Count Florent of Holland, their relationship with Saxony, other things; in the meantime, Richenza was no longer in any case seen about Court, being kept from him in seclusion. He should have known that it was a fool's dream, that all the Court would hold its sides with laughter when they heard; a middle-aged man to aspire to wed his own niece! The Duchess of Saxony must herself have known, and have kept her daughter close by her; they were subtle, all these Plantagenets, not showing their thoughts unless it suited them, and then the men at any rate, when they were angered, chewed straw. Fool! Fool! He would ride home.

He signified as much to Henry. 'Do not go yet,' the King of England said persuasively. 'While you are here with us, you must be married. I have a wife to give you who will be nearer your age, though by no means past childbearing; she is well born, kin to Leicester –' he smiled, as if the late happenings were of no consequence – 'and accordingly to yourself through your grandmother only, so no dispensation is needed this time.' He slapped William on the shoulder in the way the King of Scots now loathed. 'You saw the lady herself the other day, reading to the rest,' he said. He did not mention his queen and of how he knew of the matter; sooner or later, Henry of Anjou knew everything.

William tried to remember what the reader on that occasion had looked like, and could not; he recalled a quiet clear voice.

'Her name,' continued the King, 'is Ermengarde de Beaumont. A daughter of Charlemagne was called so. The family has distinguished itself since my grandfather's time. She herself is pious, they tell me, also wise; she will advise you, my friend, for your good. You are too greatly given to impulse, as we both know.' He sounded almost fatherly. William heard with increasing rage that for her dower, this paragon chosen for him was to be given, of all things, the castle of Edinburgh. To hold Edinburgh Castle in right of one's wife! A wife, at that, not of the highest birth, whatever Henry might say: her father had been a mere viscount, which meant no more than one of Henry's appointed sheriffs. Her ancestors had moreover been the pair of place-seeking twins about King Beauclerc, Waleran de Beaumont and his brother Robert the Hunchback. Those two had feathered their nests well enough. There had been a justiciar and a Norman bishop, and this Ermengarde's own grandmother – William ground his teeth – had been one more of Henry Beauclerc's twenty bastards, placed so advantageously in marriage up and down the land. Ermengarde de Beaumont could keep her wise advice to herself; he would use her instead in a way that would show her who was master. He would in fact have refused the marriage, but knew it was impossible to seek a bride without Henry's leave, and time was passing. He must agree to fashion Beaumont heirs for Scotland.

King Henry was saying placidly now that he would make over Woodstock itself for the wedding festivities and take himself off immediately after the ceremony to Marlborough in Wiltshire. 'As the bridegroom, my palace is yours for the time,' he said, smiling placidly. 'Hunt the game in my forests by day, and spend the nights as you know well enough how to do. In due time, you shall ride north with your bride, and make your entry together into Edinburgh.'

That should never happen, William swore. He would marry and bed the woman and thereafter send her north alone, to receive the keys of her own dower-castle and, by grace and favour, no doubt admit him when he himself chose to appear. Already he resented Ermengarde de Beaumont fiercely. Richenza had gone; it was folly to remember that episode, or the happy hour they had spent together in the maze and in Fair Rosamund's pavilion. Fool! Fool!

'Sire, I am sorry you could not have the bride you wanted. The child was fond of you.'

Ermengarde, Queen of Scots, spoke shyly, anxious to comfort this scowling bridegroom to whom she had been married in decreed pomp earlier that day. She had been bedded now by her women, and the tipsy crowd had left the chamber; she lay waiting for her husband. To her, he was and always would be less of a king than a man; an unhappy and, no doubt, an angry man; angry at present with herself for not being Richenza of Saxony. He turned to her savagely, seeing only a blur instead of her face; he also had drunk deep of Henry's wine. She had, he noted, covered her breasts; he would handle them presently, and take his wife by licence of his overlord. The Queen of Scots, a sheriff's daughter! It suited Henry well enough that there should be no further foreign alliances for Scotland, as had happened in his brother Malcolm's reign.

He recalled a thing John Lackland, Henry's unspeakable youngest son, had told him, the latter having returned foolishly from Ireland where his father had intended he should reign as king. That would get no further than the crown of peacock's feathers the Pope had sent: John and his companions had offended friendly Irish chiefs by pulling their beards, and not all the chiefs had been friendly even before it happened.

'My father can lay any woman on her back,' Lackland had boasted. 'None are safe from him, his sons' wives least of all, though poor Henry's widow Marguerite is Queen of Hungary now, too far off, ha, ha. As for Richard's Alais, Marguerite's sister, everyone knows of *that*; and Geoffrey's Constance, your own niece of Brittany, had hardly given birth to her son Arthur after his father's death when mine climbed into her bed. Now he has married her off to the Avranchin whether she will or no, to guard the border.'

He was eighteen, and had he been older William would have taken him by the throat; as it was, he had turned away without answering, for Constance's sake; to make any ado about the matter would harm her name. Now –

He approached the bed, and this Ermengarde. 'Has King Henry had your maidenhead, madam?' he asked her. 'If I find that it is so, your sides will smart, I promise.'

'No man has taken me,' she answered quietly.

'Then I will do so.' He came into bed then and took her, finding the maidenhead intact and breaking it. Thereafter he used her without mercy. He was still somewhat drunk. At the end he said to her, still coldly, 'Now that you are my wife, he may still attempt you: such exploits give him pleasure. You will keep yourself close among your women. Do not ride out to the hunt tomorrow. It is possible that already, unless you are barren, you carry my heir. Guard yourself accordingly.'

He heard his own voice, loud in the silence of their chamber. It was possible, he thought, that Henry had tricked him with a barren bride; nothing was impossible to such a man. Why had she not been married earlier? He asked her concerning it.

'Sire, I was caring for my mother, who ailed for long, and would not part with me.' She spoke evenly, despite the hurt he had wrought in her.

It was a reasonable answer; presently he took her again, aware that he had been unjust to her but not greatly caring. Henry had, as he said, left Woodstock following the ceremony, and should now be on his way to Marlborough and, later, Reading. Before he, William, left for the north he would visit the King of England there. He had a word still to say.

He stayed on at Woodstock meantime for his own bridal rejoicings, which King Henry had arranged without stint; it would be noted by everyone that he was most generous to his erstwhile enemy. As for Ermengarde, Queen of Scots, she kept her chamber and obeyed her husband. William had to admit that she was correct in all her behaviour. No doubt she hoped to cozen him with the Beaumont slyness: one recalled Leicester, turning coat at Falaise. He continued to use his bride nightly to the full, flushed as he himself was constantly with Henry's Gascon wine. The sheriff's daughter should carry out her duties as soon as might be: this was one matter over which no one except he, her husband, had any jurisdiction: and at the least – William comforted himself at times with this thought – he had proved to Ermengarde de Beaumont that he was, after all, a man.

The Queen of Scots was duly seen off by her husband, to travel by litter north, escorted by her brother Roger, a churchman, and a fair following. William, freed meantime, then rode to London. He found his son Robert well grown there, made love after a fashion to Robert's mother – she had grown coarse, and left to himself William would not now have been attracted to her, but it was one more way of asserting his independence – and then announced that he would take the boy back with him to Scotland. The Beaumonts could endure Robert's presence at Court whether they would or not.

'God's love, what a man you are!' complained young Robert's mother. 'I may well have been left by you now with another to rear.'

'If that happens at your age, it will be surprising,' William replied uncharitably. 'Send me word, however, if so.' There would be money forthcoming in that event, as she well knew; he himself was aware that she was liable to foist another man's child on him, but he had ceased to care. The boy Robert however clearly resembled himself.

He rode then, with Robert of London, as he was to be known, behind him, to Marlborough to see King Henry, but was informed by an unwary servitor that the King had left privately, with a few followers, and ridden meantime back to Woodstock. This was more on William's own homeward way than Reading, and he returned. He thrust past the depleted servants he found at the palace, who gaped after him but dared say nothing to this large man in an evident rage: and burst into Henry's presence unannounced.

The King of England, squat and grey now but with his manhood undiminished, was seated in a chair with a young woman perched across his knees. One large reddened unkempt hand – Henry had never been known to wear gloves – was in the act of lifting her breasts where they lay unseen beneath the robe. This was Alais of France, old Louis' second daughter, sister to the Young King's widow: betrothed as a child to Henry's son Richard of Poitou, but debauched, no doubt as soon as she was nubile, by Henry himself after being sent to England to be reared. The narrow Capetian features had a mouth grown loose by now, like a whore's. Alais slipped off the King's knee and vanished silently, a half-known ghost about Court. They said the King had got her with child one year, a girl who had been born dead. Richard had put off marrying her with one excuse after another: nobody could blame him.

Henry himself remained seated, surveying his vassal. 'What brings you here?' he demanded equably. 'You should be in Edinburgh.'

Nothing would disturb the Angevin effrontery, William was thinking; no doubt his own partly equalled it in coming here unannounced. His voice remained bitterly angry. 'That was your son Richard's betrothed, was it not?' he said. 'The honour of France is no concern of mine now. As regards your son Geoffrey's widow, however, she is my own sister's child Constance of Brittany. I am told that you dishonoured her also.' His voice rose. 'They say with truth that you are descended from the devil. Your son Lackland knows of this scandal, so all the world knows.'

Henry smiled. 'The swiftest way to subdue a proud woman is to bed her,' he said. 'Constance of Brittany claims the crown of England after my own death for her son Arthur, born after Geoffrey his father was killed in a tournament, as you recall. Of all my five sons by my wife, only two remain.' The hard eyes brooded for instants. 'Constance I have married to de Blundeville, who will continue with her in the way I have begun. You are fortunate in that your own queen is virtuous and modest; how fares she? You do not deserve such a wife, Sire Guillaume de Varenne.'

'She is safe across the border by now, and full of my seed, which in general takes root where it is planted. Unless you have given me a barren bride, which knowing your ways is possible, my heir will inherit Scotland; and my brother David, who is loyal to me, will guard him even should you, who cannot bear the plain truth spoken to your face, detain me now as once you did at Falaise.' He was shouting by this: it did not matter who heard.

Henry's face had blackened in the way it had when he was enraged; he looked about as if to seize the straw, but did not. 'You speak as no vassal should do to his lord,' he replied thickly. 'Listen now; after this Reading visit I have it in mind to ride north to join you, and together we will go into Galloway, where your other loyal man, Roland, continues troublesome. An English and a Scots army will combine to subdue him, no doubt.'

William turned and went out. There was no doubt who had won the encounter. He was hardly beyond the door-curtain when he heard Henry snap his fingers for the return of the phantasmal Alais. The reason for the private visit to Woodstock was evident; so was the fact that nothing disturbed the predestined order in Henry's mind.

He returned with the boy Robert into Scotland, the Lion defiantly waving, and to Edinburgh to the Queen. Ermengarde greeted him pleasantly, evidently bearing no rancour either as regarded her own solitary arrival in a land of strangers, or young Robert's presence. She had already met William's bastard daughters about Court, gained their affection and also that of the common people, who had cheered her on entry. 'They spell my name here in the old way, de Bellomonte,' she told him, smiling.

However her name was spelt, it was evident that she was not yet with child. William set himself to remedy this state of affairs, and contrived it in time to arrange to ride north into Moray.

'Have a care to yourself,' he told Ermengarde brusquely. It was seldom that he addressed her. The wise and patient eyes regarded him; it struck him, for the first time, that they were beautiful. Behind them both stood Margaret Atheling's little stone chapel, built against the castle wall, where the Queen herself heard mass daily; and below, as always, the Nor'Loch was ruffled grey with the constant east wind.

'And you also must have a care,' said Ermengarde. 'Ride back safely.'

Why was she so gentle with him always? He told himself that he would have preferred a woman who stood up to him, gave him, as it were, blow for blow. He had however not laid hands on Ermengarde de Beaumont in any way but one. It began to occur to him that perhaps, after all, he respected her.

'If you are not a free leader of men you are not our leader. We can fight without you as we have always done.'

It was the old trouble, the old shame; also, they looked on him still as a Norman invader. All of it angered William more than ever.

'Whom else would you serve?' he asked the men of Moray in Gaelic. 'Is it yourselves, or the sons of Somerled, or any impostor who comes down out of the mountains saying he is a fool's grandson? Honour the Lion of Scotland: that shall be your unfailing leader, though kings come and go.'

He pointed to the great Lion banner, flaunting its gule, and or. It was the kind of symbol they understood, something to which to rally. By the end, they defeated five hundred assembled ruffians and slew their leader like Goliath: the bleeding severed head of MacWilliam, its blond hair now long turned white, was held up to be seen by all, and although the dead man had left sons everywhere like dragons' teeth, William the Lion rode home. Other things were happening in the world, of more import than one further rebellion in Moray. Jerusalem itself had been lost, and Christ's tomb with it. Even old Henry of England murmured about taking himself on crusade, to atone for his sins; and had been precise about the colours chosen for the crusaders' shields, white for England, red for France, green for Flanders. William determined that the Scots shield should instead be blue, with a saltire for St. Andrew. It was probable that Henry himself would never ride on crusade; but his son Richard was on fire to do so, at the same time making war on his father.

Meantime Queen Ermengarde gave birth to William's child. It proved a girl.

PART IV

One

'So he is dead, that devil.'

The news of Henry II's death in France, at Chinon, had reached them as they sat, all of William's family by many mothers, and the Queen who was heavy a second time with child, in the little sheltered garden high in Edinburgh Castle, where as a rule nothing but ivy grew. Now, the tiny princess Margaret crawled by herself among daisies on the grass. Her mother the Queen and the latter's stepdaughters, Ada de Dunbar, Isabel de Brus, an elder Margaret recently married to de Vesci, and young Africa, newly betrothed to William de Say, were sewing an altarcloth together for the chapel on the wall. Ermengarde was kind to all her stepchildren. The gold thread glinted as they sewed in the sunlight. It was rare to have so fine a day.

William himself had been feeling faintly patriarchal, also guilty for a reason he hoped would not have to be disclosed. It had happened on the other side of Scotland, at a place called Ibrox, not far from Glasgow. He had simply found that he needed a woman, and during Ermengarde's pregnancies did not touch her lest he unwittingly harm the heir; so he had taken one girl, of a family whose very name should have warned him to be careful; Galightly. Now, the young woman in question had sent word that she was with child by him. He had already resolved in any case to mend his ways. Ermengarde might be kindness itself to his daughters and to young Robert, who was also in the garden with them; but it might well be a different matter with news of a bastard got after their marriage, especially while she was in her present state. Moreover, though William told himself he would still not be cozened by any Beaumont, he had himself named the Queen's brother, Roger, as next Archbishop of St. Andrews following the demise of old Hugh. Had Hugh still been his confessor, the latter would have understood; but one could hardly confess the existing situation to Ermengarde's brother.

However the news from Chinon stunned all of them
meantime: the women put aside their gleaming cloth, crossed
themselves and prayed for the dead man's soul. The messenger
who had come, young Robert, and his father drew aside, to
hear the further details of the death. These were ugly, and
unfit for a pregnant woman's ears, or for that matter any
woman's.

'He had willed his heart away from God when his son
Richard set fire to Le Mans, Henry's own birthplace where his
father lies buried, that is if Geoffrey of Aujou was indeed his
father and not King Stephen.' The messenger was none other
than Countess Ada's own Taurin de Bailleul, who was much
about the English Court and also, by now, David of
Huntingdon's, controlling as it did the sprawling Honour in the
Midlands in as magnificent a way as if David were king. Taurin
knew he could speak as he chose. 'He said,' he went on 'that as
God had taken away the place he loved best, he himself would
take from God what God craved, namely his heart. At that rate,
he is surely in hell. He failed bodily in front of Richard and
King Philip, and was borne at last to Chinon to die; they say
Lackland's name on the list of those who adhered to Richard in
his rebellion is what killed Henry when he heard it, for he loved
Lackland best of all his sons.'

It was strange to think of Richard of Poitou as King of
England; he had been mostly in Aquitaine before the present
war he had waged against his father, and his government there
was said to have been most cruel, with drownings, blinding and
mutilation of high and low together. Nevertheless William
remembered Richard more pleasantly than he did his father.
He listened to the rest of the tale of the Old King's sorry end.
'His bastard son Geoffrey, the one by Rosamund, was with him,
but he must have left the body alone; they stripped it
afterwards, and it was found lying naked, like the Conqueror's
in his time. A servant covered it then with Henry's short
Angevin cloak; you remember they always called him Henry
Curtmantle.'

Taurin talked on with relish, as was his habit, telling of how
they had had to take the gold fringe off some lady's petticoat at
last to simulate a crown at the burial. William was aware of
sudden sadness. Bad as the man had been in many ways, he had
been an able king and it was a pitiful end. He himself would
have masses said for Henry II. He turned away to order the
bells to be tolled in the town's street: and stopped listening to

the story, which was true, of how at the kiss of peace, at a recent mass together, the Old King had whispered in his son Richard's ear that he hoped God would allow him to live long enough to be avenged on him. Richard had told the tale, laughing, to friends afterwards at dinner. The other story William did not believe, namely that the dead man's nose, ears and mouth had begun to bleed when Richard himself came in and knelt to pray by the body, revealing him as his father's murderer. Such things were of the stuff of old wives' tales, and the King did not want Ermengarde, in her present situation, to hear them. He recalled the last time he had set eyes on Henry himself, in Galloway when Roland's laid tree-trunks had baffled the English advance, as promised.

Another, and more immediately practical, thought had come, while Taurin still talked on. Now that Richard was king there was hope, at last, that the humiliating terms of Falaise might be redeemed. The tax Henry had laid lately on England for the coming crusade, known as the Saladin Tithe, had been resented and had not raised enough by far; Richard might well be glad of money. Richard was also his, William's, friend. He would send old Taurin south again with an offer of ransom, naming a good large sum; and Scotland would be freed. He would have the Pope's backing regarding it: with a succession of short-lived pontiffs, the land herself had for some time been under the direct protection of the Holy See. Taurin would say all of that, no doubt, to the new King of England if Richard did not know already. William watched the man ride off, to the sound of the deep bells tolling in Edinburgh and down to Haddington, his mother's town. The news would thereby spread of the death at Chinon, the burial at Fontevrault. It was still hard to think of Henry Plantagenet as dead: one recalled a young man with a gold broomcod brooch in his cap, a thick neck and big neglected hands.

Two

Richard was crowned King of England to the wild acclaim of subjects who would hardly ever set eyes on him again, but who respected his physique and courage and were unaware of his cruelty. Carrying the sword of state before him at the crowning was David of Huntingdon, the King of Scots' brother and, so far, his heir; Queen Ermengarde had given birth to a second daughter they called Isabel, after her favourite stepchild.

William himself rode down with a train to Canterbury by November. This time, the Lion banner blazed with assured confidence on the wind: ten thousand merks had been agreed as the purchase price of the renewed independence of Scotland. As had been foreseen, Richard needed the money to go on crusade, his heart's desire.

The King of Scots saw the towers and spires of Becket's cathedral town rise, in especial the Tower of the Archangel with its gold flying figure surmounting all. Presently he beheld King Richard's remembered yellow head, surmounted by its crown. The two monarchs embraced one another. Richard then signed away the disgrace of Falaise with a flourish.

William had cast an eye over the clauses already, scanning them closely to see that there was no fault therein. Despite his early training in Earl Henry's lifetime, he was no scholar, but understood what he saw if he took long enough. A stray thought entered his mind meantime about a remark of Roger de Beaumont's concerning the old legend of Malcolm's virginity, now hallowed in Scotland: the mention in the Kelso charter of an illegitimate son was put down to some clerk's mistake: the dead King must, Roger the Archbishop insisted, have meant his father's body, Earl Henry's, lying in state at Innerleithen on its journey to burial at Kelso. Only a careless clerk, or one drunk, would however in William's opinion put *filii* when he meant *patris*, and in any case Malcolm himself had been only ten when their father had died. His brother had let

140

the matter go, knowing notwithstanding what he knew and had seen. *The church ... in which my son's body rested the first night after his death shall have a right of sanctuary in all its territory.* Now, everything pertaining to the kingdom was as it had been in Malcolm's day, and he himself was content, quit of any oath extracted at the time of his capture. 'A captive is not free to decide,' said Richard. It was not politic to mention Northumbria, and they both knew it and kept silent.

The two kings then spent some days together in eating, drinking and friendship. Richard mentioned that he expected shortly to become betrothed to a Navarrese princess; Alais of France would be sent home. William recalled the intense affection there had been between the Lion Heart, as men had begun to call him, and Alais' young half-brother Philip of France, when the two men, being allies together against Henry, had eaten from the same plate and shared the same bed; likewise, at the death from fever of the Young King six years since, Philip had almost thrown himself into his friend's grave. Such extravagant gestures were not for himself. However he knew Richard had an affection for him; and heard of it some years later, when a closely guarded prisoner was encountered being led from one stone fortress to another, deep in Austria: and enquired most kindly for the King of Scots.

Next year, 1190, David, that determined and magnificent bachelor and father of many notwithstanding, married an heiress at last, Ermengarde herself having produced as yet no son, and the vassalage freed; this meant David of Huntingdon might choose as he would. He chose Maud of Chester, herself a friend of the Poynton clan and descended from old Ranulf, who had made over Carlisle unwillingly long ago to King David, the bridegroom's grandfather. Maud fell pregnant almost immediately, and gave birth in due course, to a son, who died. William had only leisure for brief envy, therefore; and his Queen was yet again expecting a child. William forced himself to pray more frequently than was his habit; if only this were a son at last, a son! He did not mention that the Galightly woman had borne him one, and that he had named it Henry, this time after the old devil in England and not his father: he remembered Henry Plantagenet now with something like affection, whereas Ada's Earl was long since in the shades.

It was through David and his young wife Maud, the latter soon pregnant again with a second son who would likewise die, that William had news of their unhappy niece, their sister Margaret's daughter, Constance of Brittany. David and Maud had been to Court or what was left of it, and had heard from Margaret herself, for long now Countess of Hereford and remarried. She told them how Constance had loathed the Avranchin husband old King Kenry had forced on her, and had eloped at last with the man of her choice, the Comte de Thouars, whose lands Henry had lopped from him long ago. 'It leaves her without power,' Margaret had said, adding that the girl resembled her unlucky father Conan in such improvidence; but one hoped that, this time, Constance would be happy: even the late King's son Geoffrey had not been the best of husbands. 'However the two children, Eleanor and Arthur – they say Arthur is the most beautiful boy who was ever seen, golden-haired and blue-eyed, and he was of course given the old name from legend, and will perhaps be King of England one day, who knows? – are left in the hands of their Plantagenet relatives; that is not a good thing.' Old Queen Eleanor was however meantime looking after her grand-daughter and namesake, who was already known as the Pearl of Brittany; but as for Arthur, that handsome child was closely guarded; few saw him. William forgot about the matter in thinking of the family curse. David's sons continued to die unless conceived out of wedlock; the same, or something like it, was happening to himself. How would it all end? He awaited Ermengarde's falling into labour, continuing his unwonted prayers for a son.

Queen Ermengarde moaned in childbed a third time to little purpose; again, it was a daughter. This time, the King was angry: he strode into the birth-chamber.

'Other women bear me sons,' he said roughly. 'What ails you that you cannot?' He hardly looked at the new baby, swathed and fast asleep. It was the first time he had given away the existence of young Henry Galightly; now, he had done so and was beyond caring. His daughter Isabel de Ros, lately remarried, who was with the Queen, faced him angrily. Ermengarde, exhausted, lay silent on the bed, her eyes closed.

Isabel, who feared nobody and had taken de Ros to her bed shortly after the death of de Brus as she disliked lacking a man in it, spoke up to her father sharply: like them all, she loved the Queen.

'How can you speak to her so, weak as she is? Maybe you handle your other women less unkindly. You can have no notion of what is endured in labour: you should not be in here yet at all.' She stood there, eyes blazing: she was a handsome creature, and he was suddenly assailed with the memory of the curse that ensured only bastards would thrive. She reminded him of her mother, Robert Avenel's daughter in Eskdale: that had been long ago.

He mumbled some apology, and went out. Later he went to ask what Ermengarde would like to call the child; he himself had chosen the names of the two elder daughters, after his own French grandmother and Queen Margaret Atheling. There was a bastard named Margaret already as well, also one named Ada: Ermengarde could use her own name if she chose.

However she sent word back that she would like to christen the baby Marjory. There seemed no particular reason, except that it was a name Ermengarde said she liked. She had begun to recover slowly from the birth: and as the baby Marjory grew, it could be seen that she would be a beauty, different from her sturdy sisters: possessing the incomparable Atheling loveliness that recurred every few generations, as in dead Malcolm, and again in Constance of Brittany and both her children.

However it was unlikely that Ermengarde, at her age, would conceive again. Henry Plantagenet was no doubt smiling from the place he occupied in hell. David of Huntingdon was Scotland's heir, and David's sons after him if any should be born and live. So far, as with William himself, there were several daughters of the marriage only. It occurred to the King of Scots that presently, when they were a little older, he should send his own three princesses south to be reared, as was the practice in great houses and at foreign Courts. That they should become familiar with the Court of England, with a returned Lion Heart and his beautiful Navarrese queen, Berengaria, was desirable in any event. William himself had sent a handsome gift of money towards the King of England's ransom from hidden prisons in the clutches of the Emperor. There could be friendly coming and going again presently between Scotland and England, as it had been in his own grandfather's day, the days of Beauclerc and his Good Queen Maud. Also, till Richard's queen should bear him a son, Arthur of Brittany was the present heir to the English crown; Richard had meantime betrothed Arthur to the daughter of Tancred in Sicily, but a betrothal was not a marriage; much could alter. A

Scots princess might well make Arthur an acceptable bride nearer home. The two lands would thus become one; it was strange to think of that.

William felt ill then; his health was in any case not what it had been. In realising that he might die – after all it would one day certainly happen – he thought of David his brother, the next heir, himself still without living sons. There was just a year between them, so that it was possible that David would not enjoy a long reign. In that event, little Margaret would in the end inherit Scotland. William cast about him for thoughts of a bridegroom who might rule more strongly and more immediately than young Arthur, and bethought him, for the first time in long, of Richenza. Richenza had a brother, Otto of Saxony, who might make a husband for Margaret: but the notion of bringing a German in to rule them was not welcome to the Scots, although King Richard, when the plan was mooted, had offered Northumbria without terms to Otto, who was his nephew. William knew that he himself valued Northumbria more than all his kingdom: he still recalled the time when, as a boy of nine, he had been taken by his grandfather King David and made its overlord before all the commons. That was long ago; he was perhaps living overmuch in the past.

Meantime, in the present, things fared badly in England. John Lackland made an evil regent in his brother's absence, and did his utmost to delay Richard's return to freedom when at last the huge ransom was obtained. There would be gladness throughout the land at last when the Lion Heart rode home: but, before that happened, trouble broke out once again for the other Lion, William of Scotland.

Three

In the Maiden's reign, Caithness, furthest north of all, had been granted to a descendant of Malcolm Canmore's first wife Ingebjorg, widow of the Earl of Orkney. Their descent in his turn, Harald, kin to the Atholls, had been married in youth to a sister of the loyal Earl of Fife. By now, Harald was tired of her; and had succumbed to the charms of a daughter of none other than Bishop Wimond, the MacHeth himself, of beguiling memory, left impotent and without the eye of a sparrow in his monastery and by now dead for all anyone knew. For the sake of his new wife, or maybe to show her what a man he was, Harald marched into Moray, thereby threatening not only old Berowald's thriving Flemish settlements but all the country north of the mountains.

William felt himself growing old enough by now to want to stay at home, but took horse once more for Inverness. There he met and grimly defeated Harald's son Thorfinn and chased him back again into Caithness, burning and slaying; it was the only answer these men understood. A smooth-tongued delegation came then from Harald, offering his son and other leaders as hostage if the King would hold off further reprisals. William did so, and Harald arrived with all the pomp of the ancient Earls of Orkney; but the man he brought was not his son Thorfinn; as for the promised leaders, they had been let go. William, incensed, took Harald prisoner until the younger man should be delivered up, so the elderly bridegroom was deprived of his bride for the time; and, within the month, came news of a second attack in the Orkneys themselves, by yet another Harald, a kinsman; but he was slain shortly at Wick. The imprisoned Harald then asked to see the King. He was brought before William, closely guarded.

'I will pay you silver for my earldom, as there is now no rival to me.'

'I do not need your silver. You may have back your title if you take back your wife.' He knew it was a hard choice; Fife's sister had lost her teeth and her temper.

Harald bridled. 'I will not. A man may choose his own woman.'

'Then you may go back to where you came from,' growled the King, and had him taken away again. He then sold the fief of Caithness to Rognwald, King of Man, which started restlessness once more among the northern people. In the end Harald agreed to buy the inheritance back for two thousand silver pounds, and to leave his son with the King. William accepted; he was weary of the long war, and wanted to go home to his own wife and their children. There would be trouble, he knew well, from the Orkneys and Norway for whoever next ruled Scotland; but this could not now be any son of his, though David's wife had lately borne a boy who lived, called John.

So he had thought; but he had reckoned without Queen Ermengarde. By Yule, some time after his return, she came to him with shining eyes.

'I have a gift for you.' She was smiling mysteriously. It puzzled William what the gift might be; they had already exchanged their usual presents, and the three little girls, even Marjory, six years old by now, had romped excitedly round the mock King of Yule and the great traditional log, burning brightly in the cavernous hearth, with snow spitting in it from the chimney.

Ermengarde could contain her triumph no longer. 'Sire, I am with child.' She seemed to him lit from within, like a thanksgiving candle; but life had made him cautious, and he answered ungraciously that it was impossible, that it must be her time of life, nothing more. She was over forty years old; they had been eleven years married; it was a fantasy of hers, such as came to women of her age. He said all of it. Ermengarde shook her head, still smiling.

'I would not have told you until I was certain. It was –' she flushed a little – 'that time just before Advent; you may remember.'

He remembered; the Church frowned on intercourse during Advent and Lent, also on the day of the Annunciation itself. Increasingly he had tried to discipline himself to follow the rules of the Arbroath fraternity, and prior to Advent had, accordingly, celebrated somewhat. 'He will be born about the end of August,' said the Queen.

'He? It will be another puling girl, if it is anything.' But he began to be careful of her, and to insist that she keep herself warm in the snell winds of February and March, and after that perceived that it was true, and that she was indeed thickening again. It was like a miracle; perhaps St. Thomas of Canterbury, grateful at last for the building of Arbroath, had put in his word abovestairs. One must not hope too greatly, however; David's wife had borne dead children, and she was young. William set himself to prayer, like a sword raised high against the curse of Donald Bán. If a living son were born, he would never cease to thank God.

Spring came and summer, the light cool summer of east Scotland; it had been decided that the Queen should lie-in at Haddington, near the freshness of the sea. When she went into labour at last William found himself thinking less of the birth than of her, of what it would mean to him if he lost Ermengarde; he had taken her for granted all these years, the early resentment having died long ago. If she were to die now, she would maybe never know what she had come to mean to him; he had been unfaithful, ungracious, all the things he should not have been. He prayed for her and for himself, and the expected child; and after a time which seemed long as a lifetime to pass, saw one of the women come running.

'Sire, it is a boy, and he is full of life.'

He heard, with incredulous gladness at last, the healthy cry of a Prince of Scotland. He heard himself then ask for his wife. She was well, they said, but tired; it had been a long labour. He might now come in. He went and knelt by Ermengarde's bed, taking her hand and laying it against his cheek.

'I have been an ill husband to you,' he said. 'Forgive me that. It will be different from now on.'

'Do not forget to look at your son,' she managed to whisper. Her free hand reached up to caress the grey head, weakly and with love. Still holding her other, William turned to where his heir lay. He had tawny hair, a young lion. He was asleep.

'Ask what you will in all the world,' William said to Ermengarde, 'and it shall be yours in gift.' He was filled with wonder and a great gratitude. He hardly heard her reply.

'Let us watch him grow up together,' she said gently. 'That is all my desire. What will you name him?'

He had hardly dared think of a name; to do so might have meant there would be no need. In his mind now there rose the legend of a king he had never himself seen, a king who had no heirs by his wife. He had heard from his grandfather of the latter's brother Alexander, known as the Fierce by reason of one unforgotten foray across the Spey; otherwise he had been pious and magnificent, with a collection of pearls second to none in Europe and a gift of Turkish armour made before the altar, and accompanying it a great horse with silver trappings. Alexander. It had been the name of the greatest conqueror the world has ever known, and Margaret Atheling and her husband Ceann Mór, having christened all their earlier sons after the Sassunachs, had chosen that for the fifth. Alexander. It was also the name of the dead Pope who had supported him, William, against Roger of York and old Henry himself, and to whom he had later shown little gratitude.

He told the name to Ermengarde, and saw her smile in agreement: then left her and his son to sleep their fill after the great wrestling of the birth. He went then and thanked God and St. Thomas of Canterbury at his mother's prie-dieu. Countess Ada would have been glad to her heart. The bells of joy rang out soon over Haddington, and thence to Edinburgh and all Scotland, telling the land it had a king to inherit.

PART V

One

King William heard with a mixture of sorrow and apprehension of the death of King Richard at the siege of Chaluz, when an arrow intended for his heart had pierced his shoulder, which then mortified, making death painful and slow. Richard had left no heirs; it was whispered by those who knew such things that his marriage to Berengaria of Navarre had never been consummated, and that the Lion Heart himself had been, like his great-uncle Rufus, a troubadour, a man's man, whether or not by reason of his disgust over the earlier matter of Alais and his father. On his deathbed, he had named as the heir to the crown of England not his twelve-year-old nephew Arthur of Brittany, as had been expected, but his brother John Lackland.

William was perturbed; he had seen and heard enough of John to feel regret that he had been chosen and, evidently, crowned without delay at Westminster. In Richard's brief visit to England following his release from prison in Austria, William himself had twice ridden down, broaching the vexed subject of Northumbria at last; after all he had helped ransom the King of England and might expect gratitude in such a way. Richard by then, however, had begun making war on his former friend Philip of France, and seemed uncertain: it would look, he said, as if he was afraid of France to agree to cede Northumbria to France's ally, Scotland. He had tried to placate William instead with a munificent allowance for Kings of Scots who should visit the English Court, including twelve pints of royal wine daily and much pepper, which was expensive and of which William himself was particularly fond.

There it was; and whether or not to support the claims of his young nephew Arthur exercised the Lion's wits. The boy himself was unknown in England, they had accepted John, and to involve his country in war for such a cause would mean enmity again on the Border and danger, perhaps, for his little son Alexander if he himself were to die. Altogether it seemed wise to bide one's time; in the process of this, William betook himself to a place where he might receive word of some kind from those who knew too well the issues involved; his great-grandparents Malcolm III and Margaret, lying for more than a century now in their Dunfermline tomb. Ermengarde often said that Margaret Atheling should be made a saint; perhaps it would come about in time, but he himself had other things to think of. He kept vigil beside the tombs, aware of the lit darkness of the square stone church built by Margaret herself, and of the effigies raised lately, of her son David his own grandfather, also of his brother Malcolm, the Maiden Knight, both buried here also.

He slept during the vigil; and had a dream. 'Do not go to war,' a voice said to him. It might have been either a man's or a woman's; but he knew he would take the advice, which accorded with his own inclinations. He went back to his wife and son, and Marjory; the Queen had begged, when the two other little girls went south, to be allowed to keep this one with her for her comfort. William was by now not certain that it had been advisable after all to send his daughters into England; it depended what kind of ruler Lackland would become, but it was possible that the possession of the crown of England might satisfy him.

William was distracted for some time from events by grief for the death of his natural daughter Ada. She had been a quiet and pious young woman, less of an open favourite than Isabel, who instantly attracted everyone; but Ada's husband, Patrick de Dunbar, stopped for the time his quarrelling with the monks of Melrose to mourn her sincerely, as did her father. When William came again to take heed of events in England, much had changed.

Lackland however had not done so. There was no doubt that the man had charm, as his father King Henry had had: it would have been needed to hold his position as Henry's favourite despite the earlier folly in Ireland; in the end, John's defection to Richard had caused the older man's death. Now, John took unto himself a wife; not his cousin Hadwisa of Gloucester, to whom he had been outwardly married for some years but with whom the Pope had forbidden him to live, but a very young girl, scarcely nubile, the heiress of Angoulême. Isabella was twelve years old to John's thirty-four. She had been betrothed for most of her life to a young nobleman of whom she was fond, Hugh the Brown, Comte de la Marche: and was by no means willing to wed her overlord, but there was no choice as John could have taken possession of her lands as well as her body. As it was, the latter acquisition enthralled him for the time; he was seldom seen to leave the bride's bed till near midday. This had certain political results; the insulted Hugh the Brown joined forces with young Arthur of Brittany, the pair of them being supported by Philip of France at last; but John and the indomitable old Queen Eleanor, his mother, quelled the rising, took Hugh and Arthur prisoner, and dragged the first, hands bound behind his back with the rest of the insurgents, in an ox-cart before the eyes of Hugh's ravished young former betrothed. As for Arthur of Brittany, he was never seen alive again; it was said he had either been murdered in the castle of Rouen, or else drowned while trying to escape from it. That was the end of Constance's children; young Eleanor, the Pearl of Brittany, was immured in a convent at Amesbury and never known to emerge from it. Her grandmother the old Queen died shortly, to be buried at Fontevrault, by her wish, next to Richard her favourite son rather than Henry her husband; and yet she had, before the end, prayed for the soul of the latter and spoken to him as her late dear lord: perhaps there had once been affection between them.

William was compelled, two years later, to take revenge on Harald of Caithness for further treachery, and it was a savage necessity to blind and castrate his hostage son, Thorfinn, to avoid further uprisings. The thought of the screaming young man with blood running down his face and between his legs haunted the King for long: but for Alexander's sake it had to be done.

Alexander himself, aged not quite four, had earlier been wrapped against the October cold to receive the fealty of all the nobility of Scotland at Musselburgh. The autumn sea glittered silver beyond the responding glitter of mail. Everyone had come, including Histilla's sons the Comyns, powerful knights now. The old Lion watched, proud of the way his handsome unafraid little son placed his hands, in the way he had been carefully taught, on either side those of my lords as one after the other they knelt before the child they swore to acknowledge in time as king. William knew his own season might last a little yet; but he was ageing and no longer in full health, and it was heartening now to witness this loyalty, this promise of a forged nation the second Alexander would one day rule. Few if any could remember the reign of the first: he himself could not: but like the rest he had heard it spoken of by his father and grandfather, and knew, as all did, that a king of the name of Alexander had ruled with justice, wisdom and piety at a time when there had been kinship, and friendship, with England.

That England lately had proved no friend did not mean, after all, that she would remain forever an enemy. William himself rode down thereafter more than once to meet King John, though they certainly fell out and there were false promises and trouble over William's son-in-law de Vesci, who had revolted, and the burning of a town on the Tweed: but they had at least met again. The treaty of Falaise was a thing of the past, its shame annulled in the late reign. Only a fool would refer to it any more.

William had considered a French marriage for his daughter Margaret, but John Lackland shortly lost all his lands to the King of France except for Aquitaine, and would have resented the match. France however remained Scotland's ally, as did the Pope; and England herself was placed under interdict. The King of Scots then had an eye to Flanders for his daughter's bridegroom, but John flared up at that regarding the old supposed homage; the notion of Scotland with strong allies abroad incensed him almost as greatly as Runnymede was shortly to do. Instead, before that, he resorted to bribes and promises; the young son his Isabelle had borne him should wed the youngest Scots princess of all, who was nearest Prince Henry in age; Prince Alexander should wed one of John's daughters; he himself would knight Alexander. Queen Ermengarde was alarmed at the thought of sending her children further into England, to John's charge: at present the elder girls were at their uncle's court in Huntingdon.

'Alexander is the self-same age Arthur of Brittany was when he was murdered by that man at Rouen,' she said with unwonted heat. 'How can you risk sending our only son to him, and the girls? His Court is full of hostages, children of his lords, whom he has forced to bring there in order to ensure that the fathers do not rise against him.' She knew she was treading on delicate ground, remembering the hostage Thorfinn, but bravely spoke on. 'The lady de Braose refused to send her children so, and fled with them to Ireland in the end, but was betrayed.' She did not add that a Scot had betrayed them. 'To placate the monster, she sent him four hundred beauteous milk-white cows and a bull, with red ears; a marvellous thing hitherto unknown there: but it availed them nothing, and the de Braose family, all of them, were starved to death by John's order at Windsor.' Isabel had told her of it.

William steeled himself against the ugly story. 'There is nothing to wonder at about white cattle with red ears,' he said. 'I have seen them myself in Galloway. Have no fear; so fine a concourse will be sent with Alexander that it will be a different matter from Arthur of Brittany, who was captured alone. It suits John meantime to have our friendship, as he has little else: and he knows well enough King Philip will rise for me if aught befalls my heir.'

'He rose for Arthur, but it was too late,' she said. He did not heed her.

Nevertheless when the Prince of Scotland's glittering train did reach Clerkenwell, it was to find John Lackland untroubled and very fine, wearing white leather gauntlets with a ruby on one and a sapphire on the other. Alexander, at fourteen, knelt before the man, white-haired now, who was said to be so evil he would defile hell if he entered it; and received his knighthood. John was, after all, still a king. Everyone made much of the handsome boy from Scotland, and his sisters, especially Marjory, beautiful as the Queen of Elfland as she was said to be: too beautiful, they whispered, for the thin-necked boy to whom she was for the time promised. The family Isabella of Angoulême had unwillingly borne the King were otherwise handsome, with silver-fair hair; but Prince Henry himself had no certainties, and snivelled. Perhaps he would improve when he was older: but at his age, Alexander had already received the fealty.

Alexander rode home, to his mother's relieved embrace and leaving his sisters at the English Court; their aunt Margaret, Countess of Hereford, would have an eye to them, and there were other young people there; they seemed pleased enough to stay.

Alexander was soon called upon to test his knighthood; next year, Guthred MacWilliam, one of the dragon's eye-teeth, rose in the north, and the Lion and his son rode together to put down the rebels. They captured Guthred easily enough, for he was betrayed by his own men to the Comyn, Histilla's grandson: and as Guthred threatened to starve himself to death thereafter he was hung up by the feet at Kincardine and beheaded before this could happen. 'That is the best way to deal with folk who want to make themselves martyrs for posterity,' remarked the King, when he heard.

Alexander was glad to be back in Scotland, with its snell winds and its mountains, even its warring diverse folk. He had received Guthred's severed head as his due without faltering. It had at least been an open death, unlike the furtive dealings there were still in the south. Queen Isabella they said took lovers whom the King hanged over her bed: and as for the king himself, they said a lady known as Matilda the Fair had refused his advances and he had shut her in the Tower of London accordingly, starved her for a time like the de Braose family, then renewed his claims. On further refusal he had asked if Matilda would like an egg to eat. It had been poisoned and, they said, had turned her bowels to water till she died. It was a cleaner death to be hung up by the feet at Kincardine. He and the folk he was to rule would understand one another well enough: but Alexander hoped his father would live long, for he loved the Lion.

It was not to be. King William was struck down with his last illness at Stirling, when his son was sixteen. Alexander waited nearby, holding between his hands the great Baltic sapphire he had purchased lately by way of the Hansa, the new league of merchants centred on the island of Visby. The stone had an incredible depth of blue colour; the merchant had tried to persuade Alexander that it had come from Kashmir. Whether it was Baltic or Indian, he had paid the price asked, for a prince did not bargain regarding such things, and he had never in any case seen a finer stone. It had been bought by him, however, less for its beauty than for its known healing properties; it might cure his father. The old King's difficult breathing sounded beyond the door-curtain now; winning the last fierce campaign in Ross had depleted his strength and tired his heart. He was seventy-one, and had reigned for almost fifty years.

Alexander rose, went into the sick-chamber and knelt by his father. He placed the great blue shining stone once more beneath the big hands; they were growing colder, and the boy tried to warm them at the same time with his own. The Lion's eyes dwelt on his son with a look of pride and love.

'No jewel will save me now, lad. Maybe even no priest can.'
He was fighting for breath, but the well-remembered grin, that
of a boy, showed faintly with the last words. The Queen, who
had waited at his side these past days and nights without
resting, rose now, her robe brushing against the curtain, and
went out. Beyond, the wind was rising, high on the Castle rock
as they were: it was December. Queen Ermengarde returned
presently with the chaplain, his cloak's folds stirring in the
draught from the opened outer door. He bore the Host, and
William let his eyes rest on it at last.

'Set the stone in your crown, Alexander,' he breathed. 'Show
them Scotland is a free land, with a grand king. Remember also
that an oath made under duress is not binding.' He tried to
struggle up, and the old anger flared in the fading eyes. 'To the
devil with them! They made me prisoner at that place, Falaise
in Normandy. I would be there yet had I not sworn.'

'Never heed it, sire,' said Alexander. 'King Richard freed you
from the oath; all men know of that.'

'Ay, for money. Keep your money by you in case of need:
marry early and get sons. Do not wait, as I had to, being a
vassal. A vassal ... we are no vassals to England and never were,
save only for Huntingdon.'

He gasped on the last phrase, his face altering and growing
grey. 'The charm will be broken yet,' he whispered then. He
began to talk, in what sounded to them like confusion, about
some old blind king's curse, very long ago. 'Do not delay your
wedding,' he breathed again. 'Fear no man, only God. God is
stronger than the devil, and on our side; did not seven Popes
say so in their turn? Bring me the Rose, the Golden Rose; take
away your blue stone now, Alexander. The Rose ... and the
priest, lad. It is time.'

'He is waiting, father,' said the Prince of Scotland, through
his tears: there could be no more speech with the dying man
after he had made his last confession. As he and his mother
waited in the outer chamber, Queen Ermengarde directed that
the Pope's gleaming accolade should be borne in when the
priest made a sign. As sight left the Lion's eyes it was the last
thing he saw. Presently Ermengarde, weeping, came to kiss the
hand of her son Alexander II, King of Scots.

The bitter December wind followed the Lion's body as it was
borne in procession to Arbroath, to rest there in the abbey he
had had built to the honour of God and St. Thomas. It was

strange to think of the burly old frame wrapped in the black Benedictine cloak of a fraternity; but William himself had smiled broadly, not long ago when it was made known to him that in Germany and other places, where they took life seriously, he was known as William the Holy. It was the last description he would have applied to himself in youth, or even since. Old David of Huntingdon, senile now, rode in the procession: unlike his brother he had not kept his wits.

The wind was still howling about Scone two days later, where Alexander was crowned with the full ceremonial first introduced by Ada the Countess after the fashion of the English kings. Goldsmiths had worked night and day to set the great sapphire in the crown, and the Black Rood of Scotland, which Margaret Atheling had given, was borne, richly bejewelled, before him and the seven earls while William Malvoisin, Bishop of St. Andrews, consecrated and crowned the new King of Scots.

Alexander at sixteen missed his father and still mourned for him, and would do so many days. This however was a solemn occasion, despite its haste to prevent a Gaelic uprising, more magnificent in fact than had ever been known before in Scotland. Having been anointed and set on the ancient Stone beneath its spread gold cloths, he knew he was no longer as others: his life from now on must be lived for his kingdom. Nevertheless he felt the dogged presence of the old Lion near him still, as if there were two strong hands instead of one laid on his sword. The bright banner raised, with the lion rampant, had been his father's; he himself would try to be worthy of it. He received the lords' homage calmly, then walked in his regalia to where the crowds waited beyond the moot-hill. There was acclaim for him; they called out blessings at sight of the handsome tawny-haired young king in his crown with its great new shining sapphire. Alexander would keep the kingdom safe; a king was proved by his deeds, and this one had fought well already. Peace to the folk, the leader of the poor, they were to write of him later: and something of that showed in the young man's bearing now.

The coronation had not been too soon. After the hanging up of Guthred by his feet at Kincardine, the remaining pretenders, the queried descendants of Lulach the Fool by way of Wimond MacHeth in the third generation, and the remaining bastard MacWilliams, had made common cause together. As when the boy Malcolm IV had inherited, there were risings in the north and west at once. Alexander hoped to build a bridge of some kind between himself, with the blood of Crinan the Thane in him, and the Gael, who remembered the past more than the present. Meantime, once again, he prepared an army.

There arose hope then, perhaps an answer to prayer by means of William the Holy himself. Word came from one Makintagart of Applecross, descendant of priests, known to the Gael as Sagarts: he offered to meet King Alexander at whatever time and place should be suitable to himself. The messengers had come swiftly on foot, and were kilted: that form of dress, said to have been introduced in the first place by Magnus Bareleg of Norway, was becoming better known now since the Battle of the Standard in King David's day, when those who wore it, until they began to fight, had been mistaken by the English for dancing-girls who had followed the army. These men who came now were, however, peaceful in their manner and mild of eye. They gazed respectfully at the seventeen-year-old boy who had been anointed last year on the Stone said to have been Jacob's pillow. That set him apart, like their own chief, who ruled the lands pertaining to his ancestors, the Sagarts of Columba's time. Some of this King Alexander already knew; but Makintagart himself was a stranger, and he might be glad of him or else might not. He sent the clansmen away courteously, saying he would meet their leader at a place convenient to them both: Lochcarron. It was near enough the scene of unrest to act either with or without such aid.

When he first set eyes on Makintagart, with the sea on one hand and the mountains on the other, he knew at once that the man was honest and no fool. His figure was dignified and he wore the impressive garb of a chieftain; he might have been a bishop, and advanced alone.

'I am of the blood of Maelrubha,' he said simply.

He waited, hands outspread in the ancient gesture of friendship and peace. Alexander addressed him in Gaelic.

'We share known blood. Many of your descent are however my enemies; why are you my friend?'

'Because you are the son of a just and wise king, and in a year have proven yourself likewise. Any man can come down out of the mountains and say he is the grandson of a fool. It is folly in any case to make war for its own sake. No one knew King Duncan II, from whom the MacWilliams make their claim, as he got himself murdered in six months, and Fitzduncan's true son was drowned, leaving only bastards. King Lulach reigned for weeks only. Fools let themselves be killed early while wise men keep watch for it not to happen.' The descendant of Maelrubha – he possessed not only the blood of Crinan, but of Ethelred of England by the marriage of a daughter – grinned, showing worn teeth above his beard. 'I will be your man,' he said, 'and will put my hands between your two hands, and will fight your battles here in the north. I have many men behind me, as many as the MacHeths and MacWilliams and more, and they will follow me to the death and will not betray me, nor I you. I will see your realm in the north quiet before I die, Alasdair the son of Uilleam.' He used the Gaelic form of Alexander's name and his father's: the King reflected that he himself was also a MacWilliam at that rate. He was heartened by the meeting.

Makintagart turned his head in a slight beckoning gesture. Behind him, filing out of the mountains, there came silently then on leather brogues a great following of armed warriors, shields studded likewise with leather. They stood to order as still as carved men, but at a word they would move.

'These are mine, and now they are yours, and they will see me kneel before you,' said the Sagart's descendant.

He knelt. In the distance a curlew cried long and harshly, flying low over the moors. There was silence then till Makintagart spoke.

'I, Fearchar, son of the Sagart, am your man against all men, as long as life lasts; on my land you shall eat my bread and my salt. You are a guest and no stranger. Before I have done I will bring to you the heads of your enemies, as the head of Guthred was brought four summers since, at Kincardine.'

The King felt the great generous hands pressed between his own. 'I am glad of your aid,' he said quietly. He smiled. 'When you bring the heads to me, I will make you a knight, in the manner of the south parts.' Knighthood might or might not mean anything at all to so great a chief in his own country; but the Son of the Sagart looked pleased enough. The King left, biding his time till he saw what might befall; the Gael had a way of promising all things whether he could accomplish them or not. However he had now, at the least, an ally.

Makintagart did not disappoint King Alexander. On the fifteenth of June following, after a fierce campaign fought in high summer amid the biting flies, further bloody heads of

MacHeths, MacWilliams and certain Irish chieftains who had aided them were presented to the King, who thanked the Sagart's descendant gravely, drew his sword, and bade him arise Sir Fearchar. It was a pity, he was thinking, that priests could no longer marry to breed such sons.

The lands of Applecross being loyal, it remained to subdue Argyll and then the Isles, the Sudreys, by now full of the descent of old Somerled himself. Galloway was moreover claimed by Norway, with other parts; as Alexander's father and uncle had foreseen when they built the north forts, that land would be the next enemy to overcome. There were already separate peninsulas. If he himself lived to be the age his father had been when he died, he might accomplish all of it. Thankfully, Sir Fearchar would not meantime fail him.

Again meantime – Alexander grimaced a little – he had made a promise to be married into England, to Lackland's daughter. He would obey his father's dying wish for an early marriage; but the ceremony could not be held yet, for two reasons. One was that the bride's father was engaged in chewing straw with rage after the manner of his family, at Runnymede, where he had been made to sign a charter of rights by his barons and had no time as yet to remember matrimonial alliances. The second reason was that Joan, the eldest princess, was in France, having been early promised to Hugh the Brown, her mother's betrayed bridegroom, as compensation. Joan had been brought up from a child in Hugh's castle of Lusignan, and if he would not part with her the other princesses were still too young to fulfil Alexander's main object of providing an heir. One way and another, there was no great haste; and other matters pressed more urgently.

Two

The trouble lay with a strong Pope elected in the year of Alexander's birth, being of the calibre of long-dead Hildebrand. Innocent III, far removed from the events at Runnymede, elected to support King John against his barons and release him from what he considered a forced oath. The baronage of England – Alexander heard much of all of it from Eustace de Vesci, who had married his bastard half-sister Margaret and had helped to lead the late southern revolt – appealed to the known allies, Scotland and France.

This time, the Scots army marched south. Alexander was soon in his father's beloved Northumbria, its grey-green distances unchanged; through them, there could be seen, riding in, those lords who preferred the remembered rule of David of Scotland to the hated one of John. There were even adherents up from Yorkshire, whose knights had helped to take Alexander's father captive nearly fifty years since. Lackland had meantime alienated high and low. It was reported to the King of Scots that he had fallen into yet another Plantagenet rage at news of the advance. 'I swear to beat the red fox-cub from his earth!' The fox-cub swore that it would not happen.

Lackland had hired rough mercenaries, and now marched northwards with them, disastrously. The Border towns suffered, Alexander's army having meantime been outflanked on their march: King John set fire to Berwick with his own hands, and the flames were seen to blow towards his own lately razed town of Tweedmouth, barely recovering from an agreement to that event in the Lion's time. Countess Ada's Haddington burned; so did King David's Roxburgh. By then, Lackland had starved his own men out; there was no corn left to make bread and the burned cattle would never again make meat. He saved a priory and then retreated over the border, where he was pursued in hot haste by the men of Strathclyde

162

and of Galloway. They burned then Countess Ada's beloved abbey of Holme Cultram, built to outlast the centuries in the days when Cumbria had been Scots and she had knelt beside Earl Henry at the consecration. Soon there would be no more than a name, Abbey Town, where the foundation had been.

The Dauphin Louis had already landed on the south coast. The King of Scots, the red fox-cub himself, having taken Carlisle, marched down through the length of England, joined by many lords on the way. He spared the churches and religious houses, but had no mercy on those few who remained faithful to John; shortly he reached Dover, further than which no army could go without ships: and turned back accordingly towards London, there to meet the King of France's heir. He knelt to the narrow-mouthed young man for the English fiefs; it was unlikely that John himself would regain power. He was reported to be burning bridges in the north. Then there came news that he was dead, at Newark.

Everyone rejoiced, and the war came to an end. Lackland would be remembered as the king who had lost everything; his lands in France, his regalia lately in the tides of The Wash – only a blackened helm with a gold coronal was found in an East Anglian ditch many years after, and never any more even with searching – his subjects' trust, his honour, and no doubt his soul. 'Perhaps by now,' said de Vesci reflectively, 'he has entered hell to join his father. They will have much to discuss together.'

The new King, Henry III, was nine years old, and crowned by the Earl of Pembroke, England's Marshal. It was noted that that most beautiful lady, the Princess Marjory of Scotland, supposedly affianced to the King, was too old for him; that she was not however too old for Pembroke himself was evident from the glances he gave her. Nevertheless it was not politic to disturb the state of affairs meantime in so perilous and new a peace. Alexander had returned to his own kingdom, glad that the chief enemy at least was dead. There had been no harm in England apart from that engendered by her late ruler: that had been evident by the welcome accorded to himself all the way down to Dover. He rode back heartened by it.

Nevertheless he was still committed as France's ally. He waited till news came of Louis' defeat by land and sea, the last by means of the Justiciar, Hubert de Burgh, who knew more than most about Arthur of Brittany's murder at Rouen.

Nevertheless Hubert was himself no murderer, and when Alexander was asked for his sister Margaret's hand for de Burgh he assented: it was time Margaret was married. In the meantime he himself was excommunicate, although in the independent way they had his clergy and bishops still insisted on giving him the Sacrament, which put the land under interdict. It was a question of payment to have Scotland removed from this condition. Fortunately, money was not lacking. The fox-cub had husbanded it as his father had asked.

'The war is over. It would be best for you to marry the Princess Joan while there is peace; such a marriage will help to maintain it.'

Alexander looked at his mother Queen Ermengarde, to whom he was devoted. She did not often give advice, or put herself forward; she occupied her time in praying for his father's soul and with the company of her stepchildren and their children. He knew that she would be glad when he himself had an heir of his own; one man's life was a risk, daily; there was fever to expect as well as war. Alexander smiled, and nodded.

'You are a wise woman, madam my mother. It would have taken time for any other to prod me into it. I did not like Lackland enough, or his doings, to be in much haste to marry his daughter, truth to tell.'

'She may not resemble him,' said the Queen. 'One of her sisters, named Eleanor, is very beautiful.' Eleanor was also imprudent, and would later compromise herself with one Simon de Montfort, Earl of Leicester, despite having taken conventual vows; but who could blame her? All of Lackland's children seemed diverse; the twelve-year-old Richard of Cornwall already showed courage, they said, and would have made a better king than his brother Henry, somewhat resembling his uncle Coeur de Lion as he did. Perhaps, however, that did not signify good rule.

Alexander made arrangements thereafter to wed his bride at York, which was a convenient meeting-place; and at the same time his sister Margaret should become the wife of the great Justiciar, Hubert. It was an important match, as valuable as any foreign alliance.

Once more the King set out for England, this time with a bridal train rather than an army. He knew a stirring of curiosity at the prospect of setting eyes on his bride. It had taken a deal of bargaining to have Joan Plantagenet brought across from France, and he would not have been content with one of her younger sisters; the main object of this marriage was to make an heir soon, as his father had urged. He had already delayed overlong in following the Lion's instructions. He admitted to himself that he liked his freedom; after any man had a wife, it was never the same.

PART VI

One

Joan of England, Lackland's daughter, eldest sister of Henry III and for some days lately the bride of the King of Scots, stared listlessly ahead at the changing landscape now that the towers of York, with its ringing of bells and joyous feastings, pipers and dancing in the Archbishop's great hall, and the double wedding itself, had been left behind. Her red-haired bridegroom rode beside her; he had been considerate, was young and handsome, but Joan could feel no urge to turn and smile at him; she preferred her own thoughts, which were as usual sullen. This was, she knew, the fault of her upbringing, which had not been according to custom and, as things had turned out by the end, unfortunate.

As always she was assailed with fierce shyness and a sense of her own lack of whatever was needed by anyone at any particular time. At the wedding itself, she hadn't even been the only bride; everyone had exclaimed at the good looks of the other, this King's eldest sister Margaret, who had been married to Hubert de Burgh, the Justiciar, who was still, as Henry her brother was only fourteen, more important than the King himself in England. There had been another Scots princess there, named Marjory, who was so beautiful heads turned to look at her even during the exchange of vows by the bridal couples. Marjory was supposed to be married to Henry himself in due course, but was too old for him. 'The Earl of Pembroke kept close to her as though they were already betrothed,' thought Joan enviously. She herself had been taken up to the altar on young King Henry's arm, they being almost strangers to one another, not having met since early childhood.

Strangers. In Scotland, there would be nothing familiar left. The only home she knew had been Lusignan, Count Hugh's castle, before the Queen had come herself and married him. One's mother, a widow, marrying the man to whom one had

169

from the beginning been betrothed! It was, as she had told herself earlier, unusual.

Joan knew she would never see the Comte de la Marche again, except perhaps as her mother's husband if they by chance crossed the Channel on a visit. He, the handsome dark-skinned nobleman known as Hugh the Brown because he was all that colour, brown skin and eyes, brown hair and beard, had been kind to her as a child, when she was first sent over as indemnity for the lack of her mother, who herself was to have been Count Hugh's bride. She, Joan, was then reared as befitted the future Lady of Lusignan, taught the things a castellan's wife needed to know, the names of the servants and tenants, embroidery, the understanding of spices and use of money and how to smock a man's shirt neatly. The Comte himself had been kind to her, had taken her on his knee when she was a small child and had told her how long ago he had hoped to marry her mother Isabelle d'Angoulême, but that her father King John of England had carried Isabelle off instead for himself. 'I was so angry I made war,' the Comte said then, and the brown eyes brooded. He had not told Joan, though she heard of it later, of the humiliating ride later on in ox-carts with his own hands tied, and four hundred Poitevin knights, who were to be starved to death, while Arthur of Brittany their leader was taken prisoner and never seen alive by anyone again. She had heard of that later; but meanwhile the Comte merely said that they had sent him herself, little Joan, to rear, and that when she grew up they would be married and she would cheer him somewhat for the loss of her mother. Joan had resolved to do this, and to please the Comte in every way. Meantime she had run heedlessly about the castle chattering French with her ladies, having lessons from her tutor and learning about the great fief of La Marche, the greatest in France after Angoulême itself.

Then came the news that her father, King John, had died. Joan could feel no grief, as she had hardly known him; the Comte himself was like a father to her. There were masses said and Joan was instructed to pray for King John's soul, and had done so without much feeling; one prayed for all dead persons whether one knew them or not.

Then, suddenly, everything had changed. A beautiful demanding woman had come to La Marche, none other than Joan's own mother the widowed Queen of England, Isabelle d'Angoulême herself. She had swept into the room where Joan sat meantime with the Comte, had ignored her daughter and had cast her arms instead about Count Hugh, enveloping him in the folds of her scented silks. Joan could remember the words she then spoke as if they had been seared into her own mind with hot irons.

'Believe me, I loathed his bed. I have never loved any man but yourself. I am free now and we can marry. I will tell them –' she had put her head to one side provocatively then, and laughed, surveying the man already once again in her toils – 'I will tell them in England it is the sacrifice I am making for the sake of peace. There is still discontent over there with France.'

Somebody then had remembered about Joan and she had been taken away. Without delay – she had been present at the ceremony in the castle chapel – Count Hugh and her mother had been married.

And after that Joan had been ignored, less out of cruelty than by reason of the delight the reunited lovers took in one another. It was evident from the servants' talk that Queen Isabelle and no other ruled Lusignan; the Comte obeyed her in all things. Soon she was with child by him, and the child was born, and then another. Joan grew up ungracefully, neither child nor woman, unsure of a world in which everything had been cut from under her feet; not knowing what was to happen to her, if anything ever did.

Then word had come, of a kind. It appeared that her brother King Henry, young as he was, had been trying to insist on his rights as overlord of Scotland, and had failed, and it had almost led to war: but Hubert de Burgh, the Justiciar, had made peace and had been rewarded by the hand of the Scots King's sister Margaret. She, Joan, was to become the bride of the young King of Scots himself. There had been some trouble with the Pope 'but there is always that. It can be got over with money,' said Queen Isabelle, smiling idly; she was content and lazy these days, thankful to be rid of a hateful husband and predictably pleased with her new one. Hugh did exactly as she bade him and was a satisfactory lover. Joan, who was somewhat in the way, had best be got rid of now the opportunity arose. The Queen saw her daughter off with hastily prepared bride-clothes and some thankfulness; one never knew to what dangers a young girl about the place would give rise, and she herself was ageing; one could see it in the glass, and after bearing five children unwillingly to Lackland, youth had gone, never to return.

Joan therefore set out to meet an unknown bridegroom and to travel to a strange land about which she knew very little except that there were constant wars between it and England, her brother's country. When she set eyes on young King Henry III, it was without enthusiasm; he was thin-necked and indecisive, in no way comparable to the glorious Count Hugh. Neither was her bridegroom, glimpsed for the first time when Henry led her at last, her hand on his weak raised wrist, up to the altar, with Margaret of Scotland, resplendent in her own long-prepared bride-clothes, walking on the other side and known already to everyone, having been at the English Court for most of her life. Joan felt more of an outcast at her bridal than ever before; even in the act of exchanging rings, under a cloth held by the Archbishop himself, with the red-haired King of Scots. He was not unhandsome, but nobody she knew. She felt the same during and after the wedding night. Alexander's shy approaches did not stir her except that the loss of her maidenhead hurt, and Joan still resented it.

Now, some days later, here were the mountains. They were unlike anything seen before. Alexander, still trying to reassure his bride, turned to her pleasantly and said 'We are over the border now. This is the land of which you are Queen.'

It was cold despite the June weather. Joan thought the people who stood and stared along the way looked wild, hostile and strangely clad. She longed for France, for a warm and civil country that she knew. She shivered a little. This was Scotland, evidently; and as he had said, she was now its Queen.

Two

Alexander was to find little joy in his English marriage, except that it pleased his lords and people that peace was now surely made between the north and south after the late unlamented Lackland's raids and burnings. However Joan seemed indifferent to him, as much so after time passed as at the beginning: he could not get to know her, and to take her physically as his wife, at which times she seemed to withdraw further still, embarrassed him. He continued to do his duty by her and to hope that when they conceived a child together, she might grow more trustful. However the months passed and there was no sign. Queen Ermengarde would have been kind to Joan, as she was kind to everyone, and would have taken the withdrawn young woman under her wing: but Joan rebuffed her, and Alexander was angry.

'You will use my mother with courtesy, even if you deny it to myself,' he told her, adding that she could remember that the de Beaumont blood was as good as her own. This he knew was an unworthy argument, but she had never confided in him enough for him to know that her withdrawals were not due to some notion that she was superior, and in any case he did not add that his own blood was more ancient than either. In fact, at the marriage ceremony he had met with a de Warenne cousin, the eldest son of Hameline Plantagenet and poor Isabel. This latest William had changed his name back to de Warenne, and was known, along with the inherited Surrey title, as Cognatus Regis, young Henry seeming to have a fancy for him. Alexander himself had not taken greatly to either of them.

Meantime, there were other troubles with which to contend besides that of his marriage: uprisings again in the north and also in Argyll. As soon as might be the King assembled an army, and set out by sea. He knew some relief at being free of Joan for the time. She was still not pregnant.

There was however trouble with the weather as well: the ship he was in rocked dangerously. Having struggled against the wind for some days she put in at last at Glasgow, the pleasant little-known green place seldom visited since Somerled's raids except for the shrine of St. Kentigern, who had lived by the Molendinar burn and had, as all knew, been visited in his lifetime by the great Columba. Alexander went to the shrine and knelt and prayed for his marriage, for a son from it soon, and last of all for victory over this latest descendant of William Fitzduncan who called himself, unaccountably, MacGeogheghan: the Irish had involved themselves in the matter by way of help from England. This personage and the men of the isles, under their leader Roderic, were in revolt, and Alexander knew well enough that fire and sword would be spreading in the north while he lingered here, stranded by the weather and, by this time, the season. He returned home perforce, with winter coming on, and vowed to set out immediately in the spring.

Joan was still not with child when he left her a second time. He was uncertain by now whether her barrenness was her own fault or his. Meantime he was fiercely resolved to settle the northern differences at any rate. The Conqueror, in Ceann Mór's time, had been turned back at Abernethy at last by the sight of mountains the like of which he had never before seen. He, Alexander, would be deterred by nothing, bogs, rivers or valleys. Bogs he would skirt, rivers he would ford, defiles he would enter till their mysteries were laid open and their lurking ruffians overcome. Nothing must stop his advance, because otherwise there would be no kingdom of Scotland left: it would be rent apart as if the Lion's lifework had itself been in vain. The memory of old William spurred his son on; he himself might as yet have no son, but he had a valiant father to remember.

He lay with an available young woman on the way. 'Bear me a child if you can,' he told her. He paid her well, and she was honoured in any case to have slept with the King. His mother, he knew, would say it was adultery: but he had to prove himself and had no reason to be grateful to Joan. Later, when a child was born and proved a girl, resembling himself, he was relieved. Had it been a son there might have arisen the same trouble, later, that the Fitzduncan descendants in the bastard line were causing now. He had established the fact that he himself was not infertile. The fault was Joan's. He must persist with her on return, show patience with her. Meantime, he ordered that when the child was weaned she was to be sent to him for rearing and, later, for a suitable marriage to be made. He ordered also that she should be christened Marjory, after the sister who had been young enough to be a companion to him for a little while, before she was sent, like the rest, into England.

Whitsunday was past and the land shimmered with heat. Alexander led his men back again into Argyll. Such rebels as he had encountered then were not well armed, and fled without fighting. Calmly, he gave the lands they had left to men of his own, ensuring the continued rights of each, and, consolidating himself in such ways, left garrisons behind who would guard the gift for his sake as well as theirs. It was the way of the Conqueror long ago, in England: it would succeed here also.

By Yule he was in Aberdeen, beginning to be a town again after the earlier devastation by the Northmen in King Malcolm's time. The sight of King Alexander himself among them heartened the big-boned folk with their Viking blood. While hearing any pleas they might have, word was brought to the King that such rebels as had escaped in Argyll had fled into Galloway. That place, accordingly, would be the scene of the next campaign.

It followed, and the sons of murdered Uchtred and murderer Gilbert, and the MacEachanns and MacDoualls, the Kennedys and MacAllans and a surviving Pict named Gillefakeneshi, made a show of fighting and then were, not too easily, subdued. The King would have remained to see matters settled there and then, but ill news came again out of the north; not his direct business, but a bishop had been stoned to death in Caithness and his house burned over his dead body. The King marched north again.

He came to Forfar, over the now familiar ways and mountain paths of the oldest range in the world. As it was his birthday he stayed there to rest. They then brought him a visitor; none other than the culprit himself, Earl John, the son of Harald of Caithness, doubtless remembering what had happened to Thorfinn. He was ready to sue for pardon by offering a grant of money.

The King would have greeted any such offer with scorn some years earlier. He was well aware that Lackland, in his time, had fomented trouble in the north by paying Harald to make it there. The outrage of the murdered bishop could not however be atoned for in any other way but blood, and the man was dead and Alexander himself sick of war. Seeing the Earl's bared head as he knelt, the King felt weariness and acceptance. In his father's time Becket had been done to death as barbarously as this bishop they had lately stoned: and he himself could not wage war forever. He had to deal now, and soon, with Galloway; and so accepted the offer from John of Caithness.

The Galloway troubles proved different. They stemmed from the fact that Alan son of Roland, now dead, had left no living legitimate son by two marriages. The second of these had been to Margaret, a daughter of the late David Earl of Huntingdon, the King's uncle, himself. All of Margaret's sons had died, perhaps by reason of the old curse. Three girls lived on, also a son, Thomas, who was a bastard but nevertheless claimed the lordship. Alan however had left the inheritance divided among his three legitimate daughters, in especial his favourite, Devorgilla. She had lately been married to John Baliol of Barnard Castle, and was showing signs of being an able manager herself as well as a scholar. The King took her part, and made it clear that he would continue to do so, woman or no.

The Galwegians, nevertheless, still preferred to be governed by a man. Thomas the bastard of Alan had however made the mistake of marrying the King of Man's daughter, which displeased half his army; they said it meant serving two masters. They came therefore to the King, striding fiercely, fully armed; like his father and grandfather, he noted the eelskin belts they wore, drawn native from their rivers and dried in such sun as there was: it was a mild enough place. They were different from either English or Scots; it was as though their strange land, further south than parts of England itself, had bred an independence in them which belonged to no other part of his kingdom. They had Pictish and Irish blood as well as some Norse, and had done as they chose for as long as any man could remember. One MacCulloch heiress Alexander had heard of had her own fleet of ships, and had sailed it across the bay to Orchardton to seize a bridegroom whose family had refused him to her earlier. In the ensuing battle everyone, including the young woman herself, had died.

'We would ask you to be our lord.' He heard them grimly, and answered them without hesitating.

'You have your own liege lady, Devorgilla of Galloway. She will govern you well if you are loyal to her.'

'We want no woman, nor Alan's bastard either. We would be subject to none but yourself, the King.'

It would have sounded better had he not been aware that they had previously made the same offer to the King of England. 'The Lady Devorgilla herself is subject to me,' he told them. 'I will not see wrong done either to her or to yourselves. I will not rule over you myself in her stead, but if needed I will come with an army such as I have now.'

They went away discontented. He knew that he would have to march into Galloway again in the near future, but meantime returned home to Lothian.

Matters there did not improve. Queen Ermengarde was failing, but before Christmas of 1229 he and she had attended the founding of her abbey at Balmerino in Fife together. Joan was in the south, in a kind of self-inflicted penance dwelling in her mother's dower-castles. She had subsided into almost wordless grief; Hugh the Brown had gone on crusade, and had been killed there after her mother Isabelle had sown much trouble between him and his lord the King of France. Had she, Joan, been Count Hugh's wife, there would have been no trouble and he would be alive still. It was impossible for her to feel affection for anyone else. She had no wish to bear a child to her husband; perhaps that was the reason there had been none. There was a child named Marjory running about Queen Ermengarde's chamber now who resembled the King. Joan felt nothing, neither interest nor resentment.

The King and his mother were nevertheless troubled about the succession. The late marriage of David of Huntingdon had, like the Galloway one, produced only daughters who lived and sons who died. The remaining son of David's, John le Scot, was of perverse temper, and would not be acceptable to the Scots themselves as King. As for Alexander's three legitimate sisters, the children of William and Ermengarde, only one, Margaret, had produced a daughter by Hubert de Burgh the Justiciar: the child had died. The other marriage, Isabel's, seemed barren; the love-match of Marjory and Pembroke was still to take place, but the bride was no longer young. It was as though the curse of the old Gaelic king grew stronger as the generations passed; it must be a century and a half now since Donald Bán had uttered it.

Meantime, Walter of Menteith, lately raised to the earldom, advised the King to divorce his barren English wife. This Alexander had not the heart to do; Joan was a melancholy creature enough already. Moreover, a divorce would create ill-feeling with Henry III, who was already proving himself unreliable. He had not, after all, married the Princess Marjory as promised: and that was the least of it.

Queen Ermengarde lived only long enough for her young illegitimate granddaughter Marjory, later the wife of Alan Durward, to remember her kindness: in time to come, when she herself became the mother of a daughter, Marjory called her after the Queen. Otherwise the quiet widow of the old Lion was soon forgotten except by those who had known her closely and to whom, as with everyone who encountered her, she had been unfailingly kind. Among these were the community at Balmerino which Ermengarde had founded, and where she was buried; and many a knight remembered, in his donations to the churches which were everywhere being built in Scotland then, the soul of Queen Ermengarde, *domina mea*; and commended her soul to the prayers of those who passed by.

The King was alone now, except for young Marjory. Her aunt and namesake was married at last, in England three years later, to Gilbert of Pembroke, who had loved her long; but despite their shared love there were to be no children. After Ermengarde's death Scotland remained virtually without a queen; Joan continued to sojourn mostly in the south, where her brother Henry, married by then to a young bride from Provence, owed increasingly large sums of money to the King of Scots. The King himself, among much other business concerning the welfare of his realm, had increasing cause to be grateful to Fearchar Makintagart, now Earl of Ross. Shortly the men of Galloway rose once more as expected, and Alexander rode to the west with his army. The remote land was beginning to be familiar to him: to his left he saw at last a great swathe of grass white with gowans beyond the river, and before him a wide plain starred with purple spikes of flowers. For some reason he chose the latter to pitch camp. After the tents were erected he somewhat regretted it; the ground proved treacherous, having bog beneath. Nevertheless it was towards evening, and the weather having been dry, he and his men must rest; they would move nearer the hills tomorrow morning.

But the rebels had been watching from the hills all day, and thought they had the King's army in a trap. They began to run down, uttering their strange outlandish cries; there were Irish among them, as Alexander knew already, for the leader of the rebellion this time was one Gilrodh, who had escaped on the previous occasion from among his masters. The King leapt up from his pallet now, threw on his mail without pausing and grasped his sword; but in the half-dark the cries had already increased, and there were sounds of slaughter. 'Sire, the Sagart's son has followed them from the rear, and has fallen on them with his men. It is likely that by daybreak, all will be in our hands.'

The sweating messenger was right; Makintagart had been waiting also, having come from the north parts, and had followed the men, whose paths he discovered by means of a guide, closely and unseen. By morning, a string of rebels with ropes about their necks were brought to the King. Many of them were young, and he was assailed by a desire for mercy; they had been misled, no doubt told lies by the rebel leaders. He called one of them to come forward, and the boy obeyed trembling. His eyes, which were honest, were raised to the King's face. The rope about his neck had been knotted to tie his wrists. Alexander thrust at a purple flower on the ground with his foot.

'What is this flower?' he asked. 'It grows well here, but I have not before seen it. The gowans yonder I know of, but not this.'

'Sire, it is called clary. It grows all over the plain, but nowhere else.' Why should the King ask him such a thing, after the heat of battle and capture? One hardly dared look at him; doing so, it was evident from his great dignity that his claims were the true ones, and that the late leaders had started the war for their own gain, nothing more. The boy waited. The King took his sword then and cut the rope about his wrists.

'You may go free, and all others who will swear fealty to me as overlord may go free likewise. I shall expect them however to keep their oath.'

The men came and knelt to him, with bent necks. He had had the ropes removed from about these by the time Makintagart came down. The old Sagart's son looked sour, and sheathed his sword. 'You will regret it, my liege,' he said. 'Gilrodh has made his way off in a boat, likely enough to Ireland again, and taken Thomas the bastard of Galloway with him. There will be trouble here once more.'

Three

The twenty-fifth of September of the year 1237 had been a day which did not make Alexander proud; he felt that he had submitted to expediency, and had betrayed his father. With the continuing trouble in Moray, Argyll and Galloway, and the increasing threat from Norway itself, there was little reason to insist on the possession of Northumbria and Cumbria as well; the old days were gone.

Henry III, his own brother-in-law, newly married to a pretty young Provençal bride, owed Alexander money. He had also made continuous trouble with the Pope, or with a succession of Popes, leaving out mention of the treaty at Canterbury but remembering that of Falaise. Certain Pontiffs knew about the conditions in Scotland and others knew much less. He, Alexander, himself had discouraged a legate from coming lately to poke his nose – it could only be described thus – into Henry's claim that Scots crusaders owed him tithes for passing through England and that the Church in Scotland was, as had been disallowed in the Lion's reign, subject in any way to that of England by way of the Archbishop of York.

They had met, therefore, he and King Henry, and the latter's young queen, with her fashionably short hair beneath a jewelled coronal, in defiance of St. Paul and his edict that women should keep their heads covered at all times in public. Young Queen Eleanor of Provence shone resplendent, and even the colourless Henry, beside her, had taken on the glitter of his own gold cloth. For the annual rent of a soar hawk the King of Scots retained thereafter certain rights in Northumbria; and that was all.

His sister Marjory however was happy, free to marry her Pembroke Earl at last. Marriages were in the air, some very different from others; the King of England's sister Isabella had lately been married to the Emperor, Stupor Mudi, Frederick II, taking with her to Naples silver pots and pans and all imaginable domestic requirements. She had promptly vanished, Oriental-style, into Frederick's harem; it was said that on the wedding night he had come and lain with her briefly, then got up and told her she would bear a son in nine months, cast the latter's horoscope, then returned to his favourite mistress. Such habits were considered strange in England, at least by some.

As regarded money, Queen Eleanor's rapacious Savoyard relatives soon used it up, borrowed or other. Peter of Savoy himself, having had a great palace built near the Thames, was there in York with his ward, young John de Warenne, son and heir of the late Cognatus Regis. The boy was a manly little fellow and waved his sword, saying that by it he held what he had and would always hold it. This was holding a considerable amount and nobody had yet argued over the matter: later, in the next reign, they would do so.

Joan, Queen of Scots, for once present beside her husband, sat without saying anything; her health was, as usual nowadays, bad. She intended going on a pilgrimage shortly with her new sister-in-law; it might be helpful. 'Is it not most suitable,' she bitterly heard a voice say, 'that young John de Warenne, seventh Earl of Surrey since his sire's death, is to marry Alice Le Brun, the Dowager Queen's daughter by the late Comte de la Marche, God rest his soul?'

They were all growing older, thought the King of Scots; there was another generation marrying. He, Alexander, was thirty-nine, and had no heir. He had tried to justify himself as the son of William the Holy by founding a great monastery at Pluscarden in Moray, a place by now settling once again with the help of the Flemings there. The sight of more white-robed monks – it was a new branch of the Cistercian order, the Valliscaulians – going about their business had already cheered Alexander; among other activities they kept hives and garnered honey. Also, there was a new movement from Italy which he intended to foster in Scotland by inviting certain of the new mendicant friars, both the Grey and the Black, to Scotland. He would have liked to meet such a man as Francis of Assisi, who had divested himself of everything and feared nothing. Doing what he himself could, he had seen founded a diocese at Lismore under the Pope's aegis, meant to serve the men of Argyll and maybe make them peaceful. There was shipbuilding at Inverness, with foreign orders coming in from as far away as Brittany; the port of Berwick flourished and brought in great revenues as always: the fields of Lothian waved high with corn.

In his reign, such things would be remembered as having been: but afterwards, what would happen? Who was next to succeed? No bastard of his father's – though Robert of London had given liberally to churches – would be more acceptable to all his subjects than a MacHeth or a MacWilliam.

The trouble recurred in Galloway as Alexander had forseen; but this time it was not the Sagart's descendant but an unlikely personage, his own impulsive kinsman Patrick of Dunbar, who aided the King. He was the son of the Lion's bastard daughter Ada, and had eccentric ways like the old Earl his father. On one occasion, when more guests had arrived at his hall than were expected, he had set fire to the kitchens rather than be said to stint hospitality. Likewise he was a doughty fighter, and when word came of great slaughter by drowning of the Scots army in the River Cree, Thomas the Bastard being active and the rebel leader Gilrodh having returned, the King caused the Abbot of Melrose, and the Bishop of Galloway himself, to ride to the place. 'Plant willows by the ford there,' he told them. 'There is a place to cross safely: everyone should know it.'

Willows were planted and soon grew thick, waving silver in the wind, and meantime the churchmen's presence had impressed the Irish who had come over with Gilrodh. Dunbar faced the latter at last and told him, in a voice all could hear, that he had no hope of winning against such numbers as they had brought 'and there are more in the hills.' This may or may not have been true, but the sight of churchmen in mail, carrying batons instead of swords – it had passed into legend long ago how Bishop Odo of Bayeux had wielded his with effect at Hastings – put the fear of death in Gilrodh, who surrendered himself to the King's mercy without further argument.

Thomas the Bastard surrendered likewise. Alexander had the latter conveyed to Edinburgh, let him cool his heels there for a time in a cell above the Rock, then sent for him and obtained his promise of good behaviour if he were to be set free. 'It would be better to hold to what you have, and to cease wanting what you have not,' he told the man roundly. 'The Lady Devorgilla rules her province as well as such as you will let her: she has built a stone bridge over the Nith, and a college in Oxford for the Scots students there. Also, she has a living son to follow her.'

'Her husband Baliol is nothing, and neither will her son be,' muttered Thomas prophetically. 'Their escutcheon is an empty shield.'

Nevertheless the King's dignity impressed him, also the fact that he still had his own head on his shoulders. He promised peace, kept his promise and his freedom, and went home to wrangle with his wife the King of Man's daughter, glad at least to be out of the stone cell in Edinburgh.

The King sighed, thinking of the next task to be undertaken on behalf of God knew whom. They included the persuading, if it could be peacefully accomplished, of the King of Norway to part with such possessions as he still held on the Scottish mainland. This had been the case ever since wily Magnus Bareleg, he who had also launched the kilt, had dragged a ship across the Kintyre peninsula after being promised as much land as could be encompassed by a ship with a rudder. Alexander himself would have made no such promise; it was from an earlier time.

In the midst of this, the news came that he would not have let himself hope for, but when it did come he could only feel relief. Joan was dead, after sixteen years of their marriage. She had died in Dorset, and had been buried there. As he would have done for any stranger in a foreign land, he ordered masses for her soul. Then he bethought him that he was only forty-two years old. He might still make a son and see him grow to be a man, as his father the Lion had done in his own day. There was hope in the King of Scots' heart for the first time in long.

He set about renewed marriage negotiations at once. He considered a sister of Henry III's Queen Eleanor, but did not continue with the suggestion; that family were extravagant, although Eleanor and her sister Marguerite, who was Queen of France, were both of them fertile enough. Despite the probable displeasure of England, he reverted to his father's old French allegiance, and sent ambassadors there to enquire for a suitable bride. He was soon informed that there was a most beautiful lady of high birth, higher in its way than that of kings themselves, who would make a Queen of Scots.

Je suis ni roy ni prince aussi.
Je suis le sieur de Couci.

He remembered her father, Baron Enguerrand III, in the war with England. He had been handsome and a brave fighter. Such blood, mingled with his own, would make a fine son, if it might be; if only it might be!

* * *

Marie de Couci was so beautiful that it made men marvel. She was the child of her father's third marriage, and her mother had been a Montmirail. She and Alexander II, King of Scots, were married at Roxburgh on the fifteenth of May 1239. He thought her most desirable; he was intrigued even by the garments she wore, which consisted of much trailing drapery and an elegant round hat with a brim which shaded her shrewd and lovely face: a veil caught up at one side shimmered gracefully as Marie moved. He saw her eyes, in the way of a Frenchwoman's, assess him, her groom, and knew only too well what she saw; a man who looked older than he was, careworn with waging long and constant war. Since his childhood he had hardly had time for laughter. He must give Queen Marie a little pleasure; tournaments, such as they had in the south; music, company.

They were bedded. Alexander told her frankly that he hoped for an heir soon. It was the kind of saying he could never have made to Joan, with her withdrawn silences. Marie, however, smiled, nodding sagely.

'I will oblige you if I may, sire, but such things take a little time, perhaps.'

He felt her smile against him as they lay together, courteously and naturally. Marie de Couci sounded serene. Alexander was sorry that she had missed knowing his mother. He was pleased also that she had accepted without question the existence of young Marjory: naturally, with so unsatisfactory a first wife, he had fathered a bastard.

'I am surprised there are not others,' the new Queen told him.

'Give her a brother, and she will take charge of him: she is not too young.' Marjory was however about to be married to Alan the Durward and no doubt would soon have children of her own. The thought reminded Alexander of his age.

'How impatient you are! It will be nine months at least, unless you expect a miracle,' remarked the Queen, bringing him back to the present.

She was amused and amusing: he found that she refreshed him in body and spirit. It did not signify that there was rage in England at the Scots-French marriage; that was to be expected.

Just before the following Christmas, in the season that was still frowned on by the Church, Marie informed him that the matter he so desired was nevertheless certain. She was triumphant, but as always calm; it was not, after all, a woman's only function to conceive. That was happening with monogamous regularity to the poor young Queen of France, whose husband's pious mother Blanche of Castile would only permit her the boy Louis IX's company in bed. She herself, Marie, was on the other hand becoming a companion to the King, who before she came had, she could tell, been lonely; also by now she knew many of his knights and their ladies increasingly well. After this birth, this most important birth for which everything else must wait, they would, he promised her, have a tournament, a mock battle such as was often held in her own country. He knew of a flat plain in the south parts which would serve; it was called Upsettlington. The term made Marie laugh; she was already learning a little of the tongue of the common folk as well as the French she and the King spoke together. 'Who then has been upset?' she demanded. She chaffed him whenever she could, using all her French wit. As she thickened with his child, Alexander would have permitted her anything. Marie herself was increasingly certain that it would be a son. 'He kicks so valiantly that he cannot be anything else,' she said. 'Also, the Lady Fernelith says he sits well forward, and so will be a man, and she has cast his horoscope already.'

She closed her lips suddenly, maintaining silence about what else the Lady Fernelith had said. The latter was a strange creature, with a grudge against the King because he had given her sister the Atholl title rather than herself; but the sister was the elder, so why not? Persons of sense discounted a good deal that was said: why should this son she herself was about to bear be the last of his race? The King and she would make more children together yet. They were both healthy, and not too old.

Alexander had frowned at the mention of Fernelith of Atholl. 'I wish you did not have that woman about you,' he said. 'Keep her out of your chamber at the birth.'

The triumphant roar of a new Prince of Scotland woke the King's town of Roxburgh to life on the fourth of September, 1241. As news trickled out of the castle concerning the baby's handsome appearance, his red-gold hair, his continued lively kicking, joy filled the region, spreading by way of bonfires blazing on the hills to the north and west and south. From Skiddaw word spread to Cumbria, then to all England, where two years before there had been the birth, to Henry's Provençal queen, of a fine fair-haired prince named Edward. Now, the future third Alexander would more than rival him. There could be no question about the latter's name.

Queen Marie lay exhausted, her long hair soaked with sweat. The King came in and kissed her hands, then her cheeks; she submitted passively. The delight in his eyes as he gazed down on his heir was no doubt worth everything, but she was tired, so tired, and had not foreseen the pain of labour. The prospect of becoming the mother of a growing family was after all impossible to contemplate: one was enough. However she watched her husband give his strong warrior's finger into their son's pink starfish grasp. 'He will be a fine man,' she heard him say. 'He has a good grip.' Marie smiled, closed her eyes and slept thankfully.

Her health still concerned her over the next few weeks, although the baby thrived with his wet-nurse. However the Queen had no fever, and once she had fully recovered Alexander took the opportunity to accept the Lord of Aboyne's invitation made some time since to them both. From his northern fastness, he told Marie, she should see finer stags than any the King of France owned, great forests and mounded hills, the like of which there were none anywhere else. He bore her north by litter, riding beside it himself and leaving, with regret, young Alexander to be the delight of all his nurses and his half-sister Marjory. It was hard to be parted from this wondrous son: but the King made himself gracious in face of Walter Bisset's lavish hospitality, though he found he could not altogether like their host. Marie, however, was captivated by Bisset; he possessed a smooth charm not often encountered in Scotland, no doubt missed by her somewhat after the chivalry of her father Enguerrand's great court in Picardy.

She lay watching the dead gralloched stags borne, feet tied together on poles, into the hall, amid the light of blazing torches held by burly Highlanders wearing plaids over their familiar saffron. She could recall this checked cloth becoming popular in France before she herself had left it; old Queen Blanche, taking an interest in the world for once, had had bed-covers made out of it. She mentioned this to Alexander.

'It is becoming very important here, the tartan,' he told her, adding that it depended on which plants were available in any region for the women to dye into the wool after spinning it, so every part by now had its own traditional pattern. 'It has been laid down for some time that a priest in any case has seven colours and a king only six,' he said, smiling. 'That keeps us in our respective places.'

The wail of the pipes however shocked Marie, and she covered her ears and begged for it to stop. The Lord Bisset – so hospitable, so considerate of herself! – assented at once, and the noise died down to a final sob, then silence. Bisset was enthusiastic for the project they had for the tournament at Upsettlington; he had lands there himself and would be a protagonist. It was possible that some English knights would come there with their accoutrements, he told her, fording the deep brown Tweed: he knew several as neighbours already.

They came home, and gladly again visited young Alexander, almost ready by now to crawl about the floor; his hair had begun to spring in bright curls. The King loved to pick him up and dandle him; he was in fact unwilling to leave again for the tournament. However, it had been arranged, and if it was a success they would, he decided, hold a later one at rebuilt Haddington.

Four

The King and Queen of Scots rode down to Upsettlington,
seeing beyond the broad dangerous running Tweed the
rearing pallid bulk of Norham, where talks had been held with
Lackland in his day. In the field itself with its scythed grass,
tents had been ready set up with the shields of the combatants
raised on poles outside them as was the way in France. One
device, a striking sable with three pallets, was that of the young
Earl of Atholl, nephew of Alan of Galloway and also of the
Lady Fernelith. That reclusive personage herself had not come
with them, and the King was glad: her presence disturbed him
beyond reason.

The trumpets sounded, and among those who rode out into
the field, lance balanced upon lance upon the fragrant grass,
were Atholl himself against Walter Bisset. Bisset was unhorsed
at once. He toppled and fell, rising with an ugly expression on
his face still, beneath the vizor they lifted away. Queen Marie
laughed, and clapped her hands.

'Well done, my lord of Atholl! You have *bouleversé* him at
Upsettlington; the place is aptly named again by you.'

Patrick Atholl smiled and bowed courteously. He was a quiet
young man who had not expected to win. The King had a
particular liking for him; Atholl had been his companion at
York when the bond concerning the soar hawk for
Northumbria was signed before Henry III. The boy's quiet
presence had been a solace then.

Nobody would have expected such an episode, one of mock
battle, to end in tragedy. It did not occur till the following year,
when the second tournament took place as planned at
Haddington, being a grander affair than before. Countess Ada's
town had recovered from King John's late burnings; the great
abbey had risen day and night, a lamp even yet to all the land. It
had been enriched greatly with coloured glass, gold and silver

shrines, carving and jewels, and was famous already beyond seas and in England. When there was an alarm by night that a house in the High Street had been set on fire, the King's first care was for the abbey, and his grandmother's memory there. However the wind blew otherwise, and the house itself turned out to be that in which Atholl, having left his new bride Lora at home in Strathbogie for the time, had been staying to take part in the tournament. Call as they might, Earl Patrick could not be wakened by anyone to come out of the burning house; the reason was that he was dead. When at last the fire was quenched, his charred body was found with those of two others, perhaps servants. The King came himself, and inspected the gruesome wreckage. These men, he was convinced, had been killed before any fire broke out. There was no sign of any alarm among them; they lay as if dead from the outset. It was true that smoke could kill before fire reached anyone; but there would have been at the least an arm flung out, some sign of trying to make a way to the door or a window. Patrick Atholl had been murdered in his bed. He had no enemy in the world except – the King briefly considered this – the woman who now, unless Lora bore a son, would inherit the Atholl title; or, and this was more likely, Walter Bisset of Aboyne, who had been made to look foolish that time at Upsettlington on his own land, before the Queen.

It took more time for justice to be done. The Comyns, friends to the murdered Earl, harried Bisset's lands in the north on more than one occasion, leaving smoking ruins there: it would be long before royalty was entertained at Aboyne again. Queen Marie wept, refusing to believe her favoured Bisset guilty. 'It cannot be so,' she said. 'He and Ada his wife –' she had hitherto not greatly considered Ada Bisset – 'were with me on the journey at the time of the fire itself.' She had lingered a little in the Bissets' company, arriving just in time for the second Haddington tournament.

'He would instruct his nephew John to do the deed for him,' replied the King grimly. 'He is too cunning to have appeared on his own behalf; doubtless that is why he made sure of your company at the time.'

'You are unjust. You have never liked him. You are envious, my friend.'

'Do not be foolish. There is murder here. I cannot kill the man, for he has been my host. When I run him to earth with the help of my lords in session, it will be decided instead what to do with him.'

'What will they decide?' She was suddenly afraid of this stern-faced man, so different in manner from the kindly husband to whom she had grown used. This was after all the King who slew the wild men of the north and west, who had as a boy strung up a rebel by the feet at Kincardine and cut off his head. Bisset had told her of that.

Marie shivered; the King had left her and gone out. To have to spend the remainder of one's days here, among savages who burned men to death out of revenge after a tourney! They had been joyous at Haddington after the event; there had been feasting and music, with the tired knights freed from their armour and lounging at last among wine-cups in the hall. Bisset himself had told entertaining stories as usual. If they found him guilty, he would be taken away to prison or else sent out of the country altogether. Marie was piqued, and for some days would not speak amiably to her husband. He was to ride soon to the west and the Isles, however, and she relented.

Walter Bisset, and his old uncle William the head of the house, also his nephew, were found guilty by a convocation of lords and churchmen in Edinburgh. Feeling ran high, for Atholl had been much loved. In the end, partly for Marie's sake, the King smuggled the Bissets privately out of Scotland: by his clemency Walter was permitted to make a vow to travel as a pilgrim to the Holy Land, while John, the actual murderer, escaped to Ireland. Walter Bisset betrayed the King of Scots' trust, remaining instead in England and fomenting trouble there with the weak King Henry and Queen Eleanor's greedy Savoyards. The matter of the vassalage of Scotland was raised again; Henry recruited twenty Irish chiefs and a fleet of ships from Flanders, gave land to John Bisset in Ulster, and marched north. 'He has no right to claim an inch of Scottish land,' remarked Alexander angrily, and raised an army of his own. When the English perceived its quality, there was less talk of war. Peace of a kind was made in the end at Robert Curthose's by now old fort of Newcastle; but relations, then and later, were less easy than they had been when the two kings, and their respective wives, had met at York nine years earlier over the matter of Northumbria and a soar hawk rent. There was still resentment over Alexander's later French marriage, though Louis IX had been a generous overlord to Henry III, his vassal.

The next difficulty awaiting the King of Scots would be in the Sudreys, with one Ewen of Lorn. The man maintained his vassalage to Scotland and Norway both, and when told he could not serve two masters had replied that as the masters were meantime at peace, this was possible. Alexander knew that he must set out soon on another journey, leaving his well-loved son, now seven.

Five

'And then I went to Rome on pilgrimage, like the kings Cnut and MacBeth before me, and seven priests behind me, and got absolution for no more sins than other men commit, and it was as well, for shortly thereafter there was no Pope at all in Rome for a year and seven months, and I would have made my journey for nothing.'

Donald, calling himself King of the Isles and Lord of Argyll and Kintyre, emptied his mead-cup of silver and leather, made after the old fashion, and waited for the King, who sat at his right hand, to do the same before signalling that both great cups should be refilled. As they would be full then not of mead, but once again of the strong usquebaugh they distilled here in the islands, Alexander contrived to tip some of his own into the rushes of the floor beneath the high table, everybody except himself being too far gone to notice. He was trying to keep his mind clear – it was needed in the circumstances – and also to banish from it the thoughts that kept thrusting in: one was that on this summer's day his little son Alexander, whose company he craved far more than usquebaugh, would be riding his pony on the sands at Musselburgh, having lately lost a milk-tooth. He had brought the latter with pride to his father, who carried it with him now; and had boasted of how they had tied the tooth with silk thread and then attached that to the open chapel door, then shut it while he, Alexander, stood still. He, the Prince, had not moved at all. 'It did not hurt,' he assured the King. 'Are you going to go away again?'

The child's eyes had been wistful; his father was forever going away. He had of course to ride up and down the land to north and east and west, or else order would not be kept in any of those places. Soon he, the Prince of Scotland, would be able to go with the King, as his father himself had in the end ridden with his, when he was fourteen, to kill a rebel at Kincardine. Meantime, however, the King was to sail alone to the Sudreys, the fabled isles of the western sea. There was a rebel there who said now he was the vassal of the King of Norway, having lately disavowed vassalage to the King of Scots. Norway would, if there was a war, use the islands as a base to sweep down on the mainland: the Prince understood this clearly. He had been told as much, also that the King had fruitlessly sent messengers and letters to Norway over the years, and lately even two bishops, and had likewise offered money to try to regain the whole of his land peaceably; but the King of Norway only said that he did not need any money. So now the King, Alexander's father, was to go to the Isles himself; and when would he return?

'By the time I come back you will have a new tooth grown,' was all the King had said, and had set his hands then in a great loving grip on the little boy's shoulders. 'I leave the Queen, and the land, in your charge, Alexander,' he said. 'Look after them well till I return.'

It was not strictly true about the charge: Walter Comyn of Menteith, as the boy knew, would be here as always, with good advice, such as that Scotland was not and never had been England's vassal except by force, and to remember it always. However the King would soon return; and meanwhile had ridden off, mailed and with the great lion rampant on his banners and his red-and-gold surcoat, and a following with him, going to the far places where there was blue sea and white sand, whiter by far than at Musselburgh; so the boy had been told. One day he would see everything of the kind with his father. They had done many things together when the King had time; the pony itself had been bought from the Mounth, the northern mountains, and the elder Alexander had taught the younger to ride it; and the child had already been given a little spear and been shown how to ride at the ring; he liked that, and when he should have grown tall enough to ride a charger, the sport would be better still; but one must never seek real war, only mock, a tourney. Alexander had been taught this also, and downed his tears at the familiar sight of the King riding off. The future together, when he had grown his new tooth, would be even better than the past, for the King would not for much longer have to leave him behind, a child.

The King himself, pouring away his unwanted usquebaugh in the Isles, knew all that was in his son's mind, for he himself had put it there. The boy would make a splendid king in time; he feared nothing and charmed everyone. Alexander forced his mind to return meanwhile to the blethers of Donald of the

Isles, who was trying to make him drunk enough to agree to anything concerning the King of Norway and his own ally, Ewen of Lorn. The latter had fled to the Lews, where there was no likelihood of pursuing him: he would merely sail up to Norway in that event, and there would then be open war. This journey had in fact been a wasted one: Alexander wished himself back on the mainland and would return there at once. The present son of Somerled – one had lost count of them by now and whether they were in fact sons or grandsons – was relating at this point how eight cows a year were paid by him to the Church for every house on his lands that emitted smoke. He would not however be drawn regarding the King of Norway or the latter's intentions: and a great helmet decorated with ox-horns in the Norse manner was to be seen in its due place in the hall. The women's quarters were separate, and the King had not seen Donald's wife, who was the daughter of the High Steward of Scotland and whom he had himself known as a child. Donald had Norse connections by marriage also, a fact which must not be overlooked.

The King recalled an unchancy thing about women, while the Toshach – this was another of Donald's acquired titles – droned on. As he himself had been about to set out from Lothian he had felt a hand laid on his stirrup, and had looked down to see the woman Fernelith. Since young Patrick's murder, as his widow Lora had borne no child, Fernelith was Countess of Atholl in her right and that of her husband, named Hastings; their daughter Ada would inherit. Fernelith stood now with her hair wild in the summer wind; she had never seen fit to cover it. Her presence there disquieted the King as usual, especially here among the men ready to ride.

'What do you want with me?' he had asked impatiently; the sooner gone the sooner home; she could surely have seen him earlier, in the Queen's solar.

'You are riding away, King of Scots, but you will never ride home.'

'Take your fool's talk away; you are half mad.' He was not in the ordinary way discourteous, but had not the leisure now to be troubled with her. She maintained her hold on his stirrup and if he had spurred the horse, he would have dragged her with him. Her strange eyes looked up at him with open hatred.

'There is a child's blood crying out, at the beginning and the end. There is a curse on all your race. You killed the child who was the heiress of the last of the Fitzduncan line; her blood ran down into the ground with her father's by your order. I have had it in my mind to put evil upon you since you gave my title to my sister, the mother of Patrick, instead of to myself, because she was married into Galloway and you desired to placate them there, leaving me to inherit when I had lost my own youth. As it is, your son will be the last of his race; he himself will have sons who will die before him, then he will die also, and there will be no king left in Scotland. You yourself are going on your last journey, King Alexander. I am of the blood of Madach, of the old race, and I can foretell what will be. For you there is nothing more, only a grave in Melrose soon. Ride on now, to your death among the islands; and remember what I have said, for it will come, all of it; it will come, and there will be desolation in the land both now and in forty years.'

She was gone, slipping away among the men-at-arms, and Alexander downed the recollection of her mad sayings. Her sister Isabella might have been married to Roland of Galloway's younger son, but had been given the Atholl title with full justice by himself, being the elder sister. That claim of Fernelith's was rubbish as great as the rest. He must think of her as a madwoman, or rather cease to think of her at all; there were things of greater importance to be dealt with. At the same time the King recalled the old curse related to him by his father; that had come to nothing, the Lion and he had both bred living sons in time.

'I myself have my son Donald, and my son Angus, and it is they who will inherit the Isles,' intoned the Toshach, full by now of whisky, as if he knew what his guest was thinking. He lurched down afterwards to see the King off on his ship; nothing had been accomplished between them, not even an agreement Alexander had desired about manning a castle on the Mull coast. The Toshach wove his way then back to his own, and the King's ship set sail on the summer wind, putting forth on the way to Scotland.

It was on the voyage itself that the King began to feel discomfort in his entrails. Perhaps the meat he had eaten provided by the son of Somerled had been hung overlong. He was as a rule a good sailor, but found that the sight of the calm ploughing sea made him squeamish, and turned away from watching it to have a word instead with the crew and forget his unease. Even as he turned, a violent ache came in his vitals. He staggered to one of the benches, trying to vomit over the side, but could not. They came to him quickly, seeing at once that he was ill; orders were given that the ship should veer its course and put in at the nearest island. Its green hump rose treeless presently, more so even than most. Alexander heard himself ask the island's name and was told that it was Kerrera. He remembered Fernelith's curse that he should die among the islands: Kerrera, then, was the place where he would die. Perhaps folk would remember. There was a chapel there; he could see the grey stones as they carried him in. By then there had been a burst of agony within him, then the cessation of all pain.

He became aware of monks' hands, ministering to him and laying him on a pallet, sending a priest at once to hear his confession. In the moment's clarity that came before death, banishing the mist that had arisen before his eyes despite the July clearness, the King perceived that their tonsures were of the old style of the Culdees, Columba's brotherhood with shaven foreheads. Margaret Atheling had not contrived to stamp out the old ways, after all. The thought was strangely foremost in his mind; at the back of it was the sin he must now confess. The child Fernelith had spoken of had been the infant daughter of the last MacWilliam of all: having rooted out the remainder of that race with much bloodshed, he had ordered her to be done to death alongside her father, the final claimant, one Gillesbeaidh. Descent from a woman could have caused further trouble in the next reign. It had been a hard thing to order. He murmured of it now, feeling again like Herod. His own son had meant more to him, however, than another man's daughter. As for his own body, it seemed no longer his; soon he would leave it. He heard the priest murmur absolution. He felt the viaticum placed on his tongue. His hands gripped a small hard object, his son's milk-tooth.

There was nothing now, only a great lassitude: and hope. Before Alexander died he murmured of a thing he saw; three figures, waiting. Afterwards they said the King had seen, when dying, a vision of three saints; Magnus of Orkney, Olaf of Norway, and Columba himself, Columcille, begging the King to desist from his present venture against Ewen of Lorn, which many thought unjust. Makintagart of Ross, the Sagart's son, on hearing, with tears in his own eyes, of the King's death, dismissed the fancy in curt Gaelic. 'What would Columcille, whose isle the Norsemen harried, be doing in such company as those two? It was the Blessed Trinity the King saw, waiting to receive him; he had his purgatory on earth, to be sure, and his soul now is in heaven.' It might also have been his father, his uncle, and his great-grandsire, all kings: no one knew.

Many travelled with the King's body home to the mainland; the wise ruler, the man of peace, was lost to them forever, and a child reigned now in Scotland. Crowds lined the roads, mourning the passing of their good king, a better than his father who had however done the best he could. The new King Alexander III was not yet eight years old, but had good understanding and, they said, good advisers. Nevertheless there would be unrest meantime, as always when a child was left.

The cortège wound its way at last to Melrose. Queen Marie, close-lipped with shock and wearing the dule of a widow, nevertheless was using her wits. The new King must be set on the stone at Scone without delay, in fact within the week; Walter of Menteith agreed with the necessity. 'And you must get a seannachie,' he had also said, 'and get him to recite aloud, in the hearing of all, this boy's descent; of the fourteen generations back to Alpin, then back again to Fergus the son of Erc, missing out none on the way. If you do not do this, the Gael will rise again and all the late King's work will have been in vain. Some claimant or other who says he has the Tanist right, maybe from Ireland, paid no doubt by the King of England, or saying his blood is more ancient, or any other wild thing to stir up dissent, will come from nowhere. It must be made clear to all that this child and no other is the rightful descendant of Malcolm Ceann Mór, of the old kings as well as the new. Set a crown on his head as was done for his father, and let them see it. Do all that should be done in such ways. Let them come to the child to swear fealty to him, as they did to his father, God rest his soul, and his father before that, and likewise his grandfather, the son of Ceann Mór himself.' King David now they were beginning to speak of as a saint, so good a king had he been, apart from his building of abbeys. It was almost a century since his reign had ended.

Marie agreed to do as she was advised: what was a seannachie? It occurred to her, on being told, that Walter of Menteith himself, being a Comyn, had the Tanist right as much as anyone by way of the Lady Histilla and her grandfather old blinded Donald Bán. She was grateful to Menteith for his constant loyalty to her husband and son. When there was leisure, after this coming coronation, she would take time to mourn the late King; but for now, as at all deaths, there was much to be done. To break the news to the new monarch himself had been bad enough; her son had not wept, as a child should do; the grief went deeper than Marie could understand. Well, the dead were with God, and would no doubt be met with again; meantime, with French energy and wit, the Queen, aided by Menteith, set about securing the future of Alexander III, King of Scots, and his sons after him. Following the first security, perhaps in a year or so, she herself would return to France. She was too young and comely to remain long without a husband, and knew it.

She was present, for almost the last public occasion, following the ceremony at Scone with its long recital of royal ancestors by the scarlet-robed ancient seannachie, back and back to the fabled Scota who had brought the Stone to this land untold centuries ago with her husband Gaethelus. Scota had been a Pharaoh's daughter. One could not believe everything, but certainly the line was clear enough from the time of Kenneth MacAlpin, who had murdered the seven earls of Alba after a banquet and thereby made himself king both of Picts and Scots. Little Alexander sat wearing his tall crown, glittering as it was with his father's great sapphire in front. He appeared calm, and took the oath in French. There was a dispute arising then, but not between Norman and Gael, only because Durward, Marjory's husband, was as usual a trifle upcome and sought out a deliberate quarrel with Menteith. It did not signify, or not yet, and as usual the common folk loved young Alexander when he came among them wearing his crown. He would always be available to them; anyone all his life might approach the King.

The next ceremony, in the following June, took place in the Church of the Holy Trinity in Dunfermline, which in Margaret Atheling's own time she herself had founded. She had been canonised lately as a saint by the Pope, and her bones were to be translated from their present tomb and placed in a magnificent new shrine of close-grained wood covered with goldsmith's work and jewels, as fine as Canterbury. The King, taller by now than at last year's coronation, was there with his mother, also the seven earls and the like number of bishops bearing the Black Rood of Scotland, which Margaret had given in her time and which glittered with precious stones. Alexander wore his crown, but it was still heavy for him or anyone, and from time to time he shifted it unobtrusively on his red-gold hair.

Otherwise he sat quietly watching the ceremony, the bishops in their low mitres and copes gleaming with gold and silver thread, and the lords he already knew and who had sworn fealty to him at Scone. There were Gaels present also, and they pressed close by the tomb; it was hoped there would be no trouble, for Margaret Atheling had not been liked among them for trying to change their ways, the old ways of St. Columba, causing them to adopt instead the ways of the Norman and Sassunach, the new ways of Rome.

The ceremony proceeded quietly, however, with the solemn opening of the tomb. Two coffins lay in it, that of Margaret herself and also that of Malcolm Ceann Mór, her husband, whose body had been brought back from his murder in Northumbria. Margaret had died of grief on hearing of his death and of that, a few hours later, of their eldest son Edward after the battle fought by his father's side at Alnwick, in which he had been wounded. The homily the Bishop of St. Andrews preached dwelt on Margaret's virtues as a wife and mother. Queen Marie smiled a little behind her veil; she herself had no doubt not been quite such a one; possibly no ordinary woman could be so. She already had an offer of marriage from Jean d'Acre, the King of Jerusalem's son: she would consider it, but would return first to France; if necessary she would revisit Scotland, with a new husband, later: a woman needed a man's support.

She watched the efforts of those concerned with raising the coffin containing the new saint's bones. There seemed to be some difficulty. It would not move. Surely there was some mistake? A woman's bones were light.

They heaved on, the chosen assembly of strong men, but the coffin of Margaret Atheling stayed firmly where it was. Suddenly a voice was heard to call out in Gaelic; was it possible that the saint desired her husband, the Great Head of all Scotia, to be translated with her and to continue to lie by her side? Let them try to move both coffins!

They tried, and this time there was no difficulty; both were brought in procession to be placed reverently in the new shrine. Eleven of the clergy followed: from Whithorn, that Candida Casa to which Ninian had come to convert the folk there long before Augustine ever reached the south; Dunkeld, the province of Crinan the Thane, kin to Columcille, Columba himself: Dunblane, Aberdeen, the late King's new church of Elgin and all the north parts, likewise Argyll, where Alexander

II had also founded the new bishopric of Lismore. Chanting surrounded the two coffins and incense enveloped them, and presently the covers and layered gold cloths. After the ceremony long prayers were said for the intercession of the saint, and after that again Alexander, thankful soon of the prospect of being rid of his heavy crown, walked in procession out once more into the June day and the crowds who waited to set eyes on him, their glorious young King who had in him the blood of Gael and Norman both. As regarded St. Margaret's motionless coffin, a miracle was already spoken of; but those with shrewd minds guessed otherwise. It was merely that the Gaels of the congregation had been displeased at the neglect of old Ceann Mór and had arranged that he should not be left behind; after all, the success of the reign had been as much his as his queen's. The Gael retained long memories of such matters.

There were repercussions, not made public. Some time later, when Queen Marie was considering her gowns and veils – it was possible these were no longer fashionable by now in France, and one must see to it – no less a person than the Bishop of St. Andrews was announced, requiring a word in private. Her son was in any case with his tutors, and his presence was not asked for.

Queen Marie surveyed Bishop David de Bernham, assessing him, as was her habit, not as a prelate but as a man. She remembered how her late husband had scared the life out of a Papal Legate bent on inspection after King Henry had demanded tithes, by telling him the Scots were a bloodthirsty race who would tear anyone to pieces if they felt inclined, and so the legate had kept carefully south of Tay. God knew how priests and nuns preserved their celibacy, if they did; she herself would never consider such an existence. However what the Bishop had to say to her now was in no way connected with gallantry, but on the contrary most secret and, if exposed, dangerous to the kingdom's peace. He was of the opinion, like herself, that the double translation had been no miracle; that went without saying.

'Madam, repeat this to none except those you trust. King Malcolm Ceann Mór's bones have been found in the meantime buried at Tynemouth. There seems no doubt about their identity. Those which were conveyed to Dunfermline a century and a half since belong to some other man.'

'*Mon Dieu!*' exclaimed the Queen. 'Then the good saint in her tomb sleeps forever beside a strange man! That is improper, is it not?' She smiled; for almost the first time since the late King's death, laughter rose in her. The Bishop however looked grave.

'To whomsoever the bones belong, they had best be left where they are. The least said the soonest mended. It would be intolerable to raise dissension again among the Gael. Perhaps when the King is older he can be told of the matter in confidence.'

'The saint's own bones, however, are her own,' remarked the Queen. 'Miracles have been attested at the tomb, apart from the one at the translation which was no miracle at all.'

'That is so,' he said quietly. On examining the body of Margaret Atheling it had been found incorrupt. There were still to be seen the traces of great beauty, and long plaits of what had been fair Saxon hair. They agreed to leave the matter as it was.

Six

On Christmas Day of 1251, Alexander III of Scotland was knighted at York by Henry III of England. The new knight was ten years old. His bride, to whom he was to be married next day, the Princess Margaret of England, was eleven. She seemed a good-tempered girl who would be handsome like her brother Prince Edward, a year older than she. Here at York the Archbishop himself was their host, and for the knighting and the wedding ceremony – there had been twenty esquires given spurs with Alexander – had paid for everything including the six hundred oxen roasting now on spits, so that the good smell filled the hall from the nearby kitchens. Everyone Alexander knew had ridden down, and some had come from overseas, including his mother and her new husband Jean d'Acre, the crusader. The royal party from Windsor itself seemed full of chatter, the King weak, thin of neck still and grey-haired now, the Queen fading from her early prettiness but still remaining one of those women who get their own way by acting helplessly, and still fashionably dressed and bejewelled. Many jewels were worn by the English as well as the Scots, and Alexander wondered why it had been so difficult to pay his bride's dowry, none of which, he had heard, was yet forthcoming. 'Henry owed that amount to your father as it is,' had remarked Walter of Menteith sourly. However it was no matter; he Alexander, was rich enough to support a wife: and now, he was a knight as well. Still kneeling, he paid King Henry his homage for Huntingdon.

'And for Scotland also,' said Henry, smiling, showing the worn teeth in his lined face: there had been trouble constantly with his own barons, in especial his brother-in-law, de Montfort. He heard the handsome red-haired boy of ten incredulously as the King of Scots' refusal rang out, to be heard by all.

'I have come in peace, at your invitation, to be married to the

Princess, and not to discuss matters of state, on which I cannot speak without my Council.'

It was not a child's answer, nor had it been entirely a child's thought; they had, of course, drilled him beforehand. However at the back of Alexander's mind an unforgotten and well-loved voice sounded. *Henry has no right to an inch of Scottish land.* It might have been that he had heard his father say it, or that it had been reported to him as having been said. In either case, it was the truth. He waited now, hearing the silence without any fear at all. Henry's glance wavered and Alexander became aware instead of the blue glance of Prince Edward, aged twelve. It was narrowed, cold and considering. The child took note of it. The episode passed over and one after the other the knights rose to their feet. Next day Alexander was married to Henry's daughter in York Minster, which was very beautiful, as much so as any Scottish abbey. He saw Margaret approach and noted that, like her mother and the other English ladies, she was wearing a quintain, a ridiculous garment whose skirt was so long it had to be held up over one arm, or else left to trail along the ground. However the material of which it was made was very rich.

The children exchanged vows and rings. Alexander was, regrettably, thinking about his horse: the English had nearly taken it from him yesterday, the Earl Marshal claiming it as his perquisite. It had not been given to him, and evidently had been forgotten about, or else glossed over, like the matter of the homage. More important, evidently, was the fate of a wretched man named Lovel, standing abjectly by; the Queen wanted him pardoned by the King. The two children, bridegroom and bride, were made to kneel and beg mercy for Lovel. Alexander was not certain that he liked being made to kneel quite as often; there had been the knighting and the homage, and church, and now this.

'How ill of temper you look,' said Margaret, Queen of Scots, at the banquet afterwards. She licked her fingers clean after the Archbishop's beef and presently they shared marchpane, and Alexander kept his counsel. The whole thing was not her fault, and he had already decided that despite the fact that she was a girl, he liked her. This was as well, because he had heard that his father's first wife had been an English princess also and that that marriage had not been a success. Now, he told Margaret, to entertain her, about the relationship between himself, herself, and John de Warenne, seventh Earl of Surrey, married for four years now to Alice le Brun de la Marche. Both were present, and John looked sturdy and warlike and as usual gripped his sword as if about to wield it.

'His wife's father was married to your grandmother as her second husband, and before that she was married to King John,' Alexander said cautiously: nobody ever mentioned John Lackland if it could be helped, as his reign had been such a disaster. Margaret turned her bright Plantagenet head in its coronal, and smiled at him.

'I will tell you a story now,' she said. 'At Windsor last year there was a terrible storm when we were there, and the chimney fell in and covered everybody with soot.' She laughed, showing pretty teeth. Alexander decided that he did not at all mind having married her. It would be pleasant to have someone of his own age to take back to Scotland. He said so, and Margaret suddenly looked downcast.

'I don't like leaving everyone,' she said. 'I want to come back often to visit my father and mother, and my brothers, especially Edward.'

'Well, if there is no war, you shall do so; why not?' They spoke in French, like everyone; the babel of high voices sounded through the hall. John, Earl of Surrey, munched the Archbishop's beef with the determination he showed in everything; as he would show it in time to come, when again there was war in Scotland itself. But that was not yet; and, the wedding over, the Scots party rode home with the little English bride, still lacking her dowry.

Looking back on his English marriage at the time of the death, in the bitter January of 1283, of his last son and only remaining heir, aged twenty, Alexander III remembered mostly contentment. He and Margaret had grown up together as companions, then had in natural course become man and wife. Any trouble there had been had been caused by others, chiefly Margaret's father King Henry III. The only time he, Alexander, had been angry with Margaret herself had been when she had concealed the fact that she was carrying his first child till they were well into England, because she wanted the birth to take place at Windsor, among her own family.

'Did you not consider that you would be placing my heir in enemy hands?' he had asked her, somewhat too forthrightly as Henry was by then no longer as determined on taking over affairs in Scotland as he had been when Alexander was a boy.

They were journeying at the time down the northern counties: well past the Border, and it was only then that she had broken the news to him. Her eyes – how well he remembered them now! – had filled with tears.

'Where should I want to be but with my own mother at such a time? You call my parents your enemies; that is unkind.'

It was not; he had already, a second time by then in public, denied homage to Henry for Scotland, and Henry had continued to meddle all through his youth. However he kissed and comforted his Queen; no doubt she did not fully realise the situation. Within himself he remained tense during the English visit, aware that a pawn was being placed in Henry's hands he might well not scruple to use if let. He himself was careful to leave trusted Scots about Margaret at Windsor, to ensure that hostages were sent back and pledges given that the Queen, and her child, must be free to return to Scotland in forty days. In the event, the child had been a girl, healthy and beautiful. Margaret herself had recovered well, and after that he had made sure that their sons, Alexander and, later, David, were born safely in the north.

Alexander, Prince of Scotland, born on the day old Hakon of Norway died: a boy full of promise, newly married to a princess out of Flanders. Alexander, dead; and, before that, little David, of some fever or other that killed children; David had been eight, younger by some years than the other two. His death had come first, and had not seemed so great a tragedy as was to follow, although they mourned him; there was still the elder boy, after all, and young Margaret, named for her mother, affianced already to Norway's young King. Princess Margaret of Scotland, Queen of Norway, had however died in childbirth in Bergen, a year after the marriage to King Eirik. There was an infant daughter left, named after her. That marriage had been made to bring peace between their countries after the Norse defeat at Largs, eighteen years before; the battle that had finally shaped Scotland, removing the last foreign menace from her shores. His land was whole at last, and he, the King, had thought it secure, and himself also, with his wife and sons to follow him. Now, at forty-four, they said he must marry again. He had been faithful to Margaret's memory for eleven years of widowerhood, so long as the Prince lived. Now, there was no one; only the little unknown girl in Bergen. No woman could govern Scotland; remembering the tales of Empress Maud and her wars, the same thing would happen again here.

My lords were right, and he must marry, and start again from the beginning; but at forty-four, he had scarcely the heart or the will.

Tomorrow the sun of Scotland will set. That was what young Alexander, who should have reigned as fourth of the name, had muttered as he lay dying at Lindores. He had died next day. There had been scant leisure since his wedding, two months earlier, for him to make any further heir; the young widow had returned alone to her country. *Tomorrow the sun of Scotland will set.* Tomorrow. He himself was left to ensure matters otherwise: it was duty: there was after all nothing else left but to carry it out.

At the beginning, there had been promise everywhere: he had only to take up the reins of strong government his father had left, once the troubles engendered by Henry III had been dealt with, largely in person by himself, confronting his father-in-law at last, showing strength in face of the other's continued untrustworthiness. Henry was troubled with an extravagant queen and her locust horde of relatives; the folk of London had ended by throwing eggs and rubble at Queen Eleanor as she attempted to travel by water from the Tower. Henry himself, in attempting to extort money for keeping the terms laid down in the Magna Carta in his father's reign, had in the end been taken prisoner at a battle at Lewes, in which a Scots contingent had nevertheless fought for him; then next year his son, Margaret's elder brother Prince Edward, a better fighter than his sire, had turned the tables on Henry's behalf and had beaten and killed Simon de Montfort, Earl of Leicester and instigator of parliaments in England. They had had them in Scotland since the Lion's reign, in the year of Falaise, before the King rode down to Alnwick to be taken prisoner unawares. Now, there was freedom again in the land; he, Alexander, saw justice done, travelling twice yearly about the country on ayres, hearing all pleas in person. His people loved and revered him; they had carved, when he was still a boy, his portrayed head on stone capitals, had all his life run out on the roads to see him pass and catch at his stirrup, thrust gifts on him of fruit in season, hold up their children, dance before him, call out blessings as he went by. Scotland was prosperous and free of debt and war. The battle at Largs had settled the matter of the last remaining enemy, scattering old Hakon's Norwegian ships in a sudden storm in darkness; Hakon had gone home to die then, after ceding Man and the Sudreys at last. Scotland was a country knit together. It was curious to look back on the days when, as a boy, Henry had tried to take charge by way of Marjory's husband Alan Durward as opposed to Walter Comyn of Menteith: none of that mattered now, he himself was in the saddle still, despite everything, and Henry by this time was dead.

His son Edward would make a very different king.

There had been trouble early on about the exact line of the border at Tweedmouth; a hasty Scots justiciar had held court there and the King of England complained. That matter settled, Alexander had offered to travel south to do homage for the English fiefs: he made it clear that that was all. The two Kings had met at a place named Tewkesbury, but Edward had then refused to accept the homage meantime, saying courteously enough that he wanted his Council to be present. The homage had been duly rendered at Westminster, on 28th October. 'For all the lands I hold of the King of England reserving my kingdom' should have been clear enough and was the old accepted form. A bishop, he of Norwich, had however then stood up. King Edward's right to homage for Scotland, he said, was also reserved. Here was a bone of contention; the King in his grief still remembered how he had dealt firmly and publicly with that matter. *To homage for my kingdom none has right, save God alone, and to God alone will I give it.* His voice, clear and strong, had been heard by everyone present; and after de Brus the younger, the old lord of Annandale's son – he had begun to call himself Bruce these days, since his marriage – had risen to take his oath and knelt to pay his homage, the King of Scots spoke up. 'For the lands I hold of you in the kingdom of England,' he pointed out, as if to the young man; but the real personage addressed was Edward, whose blue Plantagenet eyes narrowed again with displeasure: but he was too good a lawyer to answer hotly in the midst of everyone. He smiled with closed lips, allowed the incident to pass, and was hospitable to the Scots party, who however soon rode home.

On the way, Alexander downed his disquiet by diverting himself – it was after all possible – with remembering the affair of young Bruce's marriage. It had been almost like the attempt made long ago in his father's time, when an heiress in Galloway had kidnapped the bridegroom, or tried to; but this time it had been successful. Marjory, Countess of Carrick in her own right, was a high-handed young woman with the blood in her of old Gilbert of Galloway the murderer: it was perhaps too much to say that she would stick at nothing, but she was used to having her own way, and had been spoilt by her gentle father, a builder of abbeys: Crossraguel had arisen at about the same time as one's own sire had founded the great cathedral at Elgin, the Lantern of the North. At any rate, Marjory, the sole survivor of a posse of sisters – Neil of Carrick had had no son – had been married while still very young to Adam of Kilconquhar, who left her to go off on Saint Louis' crusade and like him died there. His companion in arms, young Bruce, was sent back to take the news to the young widow, but on the way – and the King could not help smiling here, it was so like the lethargic heir of Annandale – fell asleep under a tree in a forest. The forest happened to be on the Countess's property and she was out riding in it that day with her ladies, and perceived a handsome sleeping knight. Shaking himself out of his doze, Bruce had related the fact that she was now a widow: and instead of showing suitable grief Countess Marjory had carried him off to her castle at Turnberry, somewhat against his will, and had detained him there until he married her. It had been done without royal licence, and the King when he heard had been angry, for it meant the merging of Carrick, which his father had separated from the dangerous Galloway lands, with Annandale and the considerable inheritance the Bruces had always held in England. The latter were so vast that they were said to be the reason why old de Brus, the great-grandfather, had begged King David not to fight King Stephen at the Battle of the Standard, as he was afraid they would be made forfeit. Now, Alexander forfeited nothing, but instead imposed a fine on Countess Marjory, who could well afford it; and forgave the couple, especially as by then they had produced a fine son, yet another Robert Bruce. There were more on the way, courageous children said to take after their mother.

At any rate, he had put paid to Edward's subtle aspirations for the time; but it was a sinister fact that Falaise continued to be remembered by the Kings of England, while the later revocation at Canterbury was conveniently forgotten. Constant watching was needed; he himself was a strong king, but what would happen in the event of a weak, or none? Such as Edward would have few scruples; he, Alexander, had summed him up at his coronation, to which he and Margaret had ridden down.

They had travelled richly, King and Queen of Scots, to the delayed ceremony, held at Westminster after Edward's return from the Holy Land. His beloved Spanish consort, yet another

Eleanor, had been crowned with him. That made three of the name who had been queens of England; Aquitaine, Provence, Castile. One remembered such things now dully, and how they themselves, he and his Queen, had gone down in rich state, richer by far than any the English could show after their country's wars. Henry's troubles had arisen from more than the need to maintain his queen and her relations. Edward would be a different and more decisive ruler, even though he built fewer abbeys than his father. He had ridden up that time to visit them both, Alexander and Margaret, at Haddington, and had admired the children. That must have been before the spell of deaths; very soon after the English coronation, Margaret herself was dead. It had been sudden, like the rest; she had not been ill for more than a day. Alexander had gazed down on her dead face and thought how she had been a good wife and mother, with the sunny Provençal nature of her maternal inheritance lacking the greed, the iron will hidden among velvet, that her mother Eleanor had had, that her brother Edward maybe had also. He himself had never tried to replace her, and would not now, except out of necessity now young Alexander was dead.

If he did not marry again, the next heir, after the little child in Norway, was old de Brus, and he, the King, had recognised him as such for the time. De Brus himself was almost senile: his son Robert would make a lethargic king, but the latter's own young son, another Robert, so far showed energy. That descent was by way of David of Huntingdon, by a marriage to a grand-daughter of his. The other such was Devorgilla's son, John Baliol, a cultured but hesitant young man who was already married to sturdy John Surrey's daughter Isabel, with sons: strange how the de Warenne name kept recurring; no matter, John Baliol himself would never make a strong king. Failing everything, failing the child's right in Norway, the de Brus descent might serve: but he himself knew his duty, which was to marry again as they asked, thirteen earls, eleven prelates and twenty-five lords. He himself hoped to live for long enough to see the son of such a marriage grow old enough to govern for himself. It had happened in such a way to his father in the latter's youth; then in manhood an English marriage followed by a French one, which had finally produced himself.

A French marriage. They had already spoken of a young woman available in France, called Yolande, daughter of the Comte de Dreux. She would serve as well as anyone; it mattered little who his wife was now. It would be strange to use such a name after the familiar sound of Margaret, Margaret.

Margaret, his wife. The other Margaret, his beloved daughter. It had been hard to part with her. He could remember the girl's white wrist waving to him from the new deck of Sir Patrick Spens' great fine ship which was to convey her as a bride to Norway. The ship had foundered with all hands on the return voyage: the ill luck had persisted, there was the story of an old curse, though the bride had not then been lost: not till a year later, at the birth. In Bergen, the Scots lords meantime could not agree with the Norse, Largs itself being not long enough ago for them even by then; they had fallen out with one another, and had forced Spens, who was too good a sea-captain to want to set out with the weather as it was, against his will to set sail. *I saw the new mune late yestreen Wi' the auld mune in her airm.* That was the ballad they had made about it later on. A great storm had come, and everyone on the returning ship had perished in the sea. It was said they had taunted Spens with cowardice to make him set out. It was never safe to taunt a Scot. Now their bones lay, all of them, at fifty fathoms' depth. A few limp feathered hats had, one understood, floated on shore.

Storms. *Noroway o'er the faem.* He thought again of the battle at Largs, at which he had not been present. The ships had swept down from Norway long ago to the west, and his own army had watched the coastline all along from Ayr. After dark the fleet was wrecked by the storm, and old Hakon had set fire to the hulks; some of the defeated leaders after the fight had been torn to pieces by the men from Glasgow, tied by them to wild horses. That had been the last war of all, except for the battle on Man, now also his own. All the land from coast to coast was his, and none to inherit. It was like the abomination of desolation promised in scripture, or Midas' gold.

Alexander turned wearily, seeing without intending to do so a reflection of himself in the polished metal mirror. He saw a man still handsome, his figure trim with much riding, his red hair greying somewhat at the temples and losing its golden sheen. He might not displease a bride, however. He made himself sit down and sign the agreement to marry Yolande, daughter of the Comte de Dreux. She must be sent from France as soon as possible. He must do his duty by his country once again. Duty was all that was left. Love was past, affection and happiness; no matter who came now, he would still be alone, he, the King; but he would do what was expected of him.

He had done so, after all, from the beginning.

When he set eyes on Yolande de Dreux, it was as if his heart had been given a mighty blow, and had started beating again. She was the most exquisite creature he had ever beheld. He realised that never before, never in all his life, had he known passionate desire. It was indescribable. It was a sensation completely new. The past vanished, and his sadness with it.

They were married. It had been arranged already that there was to be no delay. The marriage itself was at Jedburgh, the feasting and bedding afterwards at Ferniehirst on the Borders. Alexander hardly remembered taking the marriage vows, or that, at that earlier time with Margaret when he was a boy, he had been thinking then about his horse, retrieved with insults from the Earl Marshal of England. Now, he could think of nothing but his bride. He was aware of her presence beside him and that she was wearing some shimmering stuff: he was intensely aware of her body beneath it. He was impatient of the formal necessity of joining in the rejoicings, the feasting, the drinking of healths: he led off the dance with Yolande afterwards and the touch of her hand made him tremble. He signalled early after that, while the others still leaped and twirled with their partners, that the Queen's women should lead her early into the dais-chamber. He followed soon, leaving the music still sounding beyond the curtain. To lie with Yolande was his desire above all things he had ever known: he longed to feel her slim breasts beneath his hands, her smooth limbs beneath his, to caress her soft hair as it lay on the pillow, kiss her mouth, her closed eyes. Did she think him old? Not so; he was young again. Instead of his life's having ended, it had begun. He was Yolande's bridegroom, her lover.

Outside the wind was rising, however, and she lay and shivered in his arms. Alexander comforted her. 'It is not yet the season of the dead,' he said, smiling against her in the darkness. 'We are alive, both of us. As soon as I saw you I loved you. Can you love me, Yolande?'

It was his heart's utmost desire; but she answered evasively.

'I am afraid of storms. It is folly, but that is how I am made. There is a storm coming now. It is a wild place, your Scotland. Promise me that you will never leave me alone in a storm, hearing it like this so near, beyond the walls.'

He promised; he would have promised her anything, then or later. He was determined that she should love him, seek his strength and protection always. 'Wherever I am I will come to you,' he told her, 'if I must ride through the night and across water. Do not be afraid any more, Yolette.' He liked that childhood version of her name. The French she spoke was still similar to his own despite the passing of the centuries. They would come, he thought, to understand one another in all ways: meantime, she must trust him. He felt her move; she was mist and flame, enchantment, the Queen of Elfland by whom Thomas of Ercildoune, an old man now, had they said been held in thrall seven years. Thomas foresaw the future. Future, present, past: the past was gone. He would remember it in its place, when at All Souls they would honour the dead: but now –

He entered her again, gently. Beyond in the hall, the guests had stopped dancing when the musicians fell silent and by now slept, either in provided beds or else among the rushes of the floor. They said afterwards that there had been an uninvited guest among the dancers at Ferniehirst, the time of the King's wedding, and that his face when beheld at last was a skull: but that was with hindsight, which no man possesses. Soon everyone, even the King and Queen of Scots, slept, while the autumn wind died for the time after storm.

All Hallows came soon, then All Souls. Alexander briefly recalled his dead wife and children, but as if that had been about someone else in another life; for the present, his bride enthralled him more than memory. Advent and Christmas came, and the Court prepared for merrymaking at Yule, but the King was in any case merry; nobody remembered seeing Alexander as free of care. In the cold of February, in Lent, he saw to it that Yolande was kept warm by blazing log fires wherever they stayed: she missed the warmth of her native Picardy. Once a thing happened to cheer her; John Baliol and his wife Isabel de Warenne, who was expecting her second child, visited the King and Queen, and Baliol – the Queen pronounced his name de Bailleul, like old Taurin's in Countess Ada's time – had brought in gift some of his own wine, from his Picard vineyards he loved to cultivate. They sat by the fire and savoured it, talking politely.

'Those were cultured persons,' said Yolande approvingly after the pair had ridden off with their escort. The King himself had watched young John Baliol's face and had decided that although he had courtesy and was, as the Queen said, cultured – no son of Devorgilla's would be otherwise – his face was weak, reminding one somewhat of the late Henry III. He turned to his wife and persuaded her to talk of France, where he had never been and where Baliol had, as it happened, been her neighbour; of the great cathedral at Amiens, almost completed now, the most beautiful ever built and already a place of pilgrimage, like Compostela. 'You must see our own abbeys when it is summer, and I will take you on a progress,' Alexander promised her; he looked forward to showing the Scots their exquisite queen. He recalled that he ought to expect Yolande to be with child by summer; but it did not matter greatly yet. 'You shall see King David's other abbeys than Jedburgh where we were married, and the one my grandfather the old Lion built at Arbroath, where he lies buried,' he said to her.

'You cannot rival Amiens,' she insisted. 'They are devout now in my country. When my father the Comte was a boy, the father of your Simon de Montfort, whose title I now have, for I am Comtesse, punished the Albigensian heresy there; he pricked the heretics' eardrums and put out their eyes, and they went home hand in hand, long chains of them, unable either to hear or see any more. There has been no trouble of the kind since. Brrr, it is cold; let us move nearer the fire.'

They talked on; not all her talk was of punishment. She could remember seeing, as a little child, the great Louis IX himself at Amiens, where he had sat to make peace between Henry III and his discontented barons. 'King Louis died later on of a fever on crusade, as you know,' Yolande said. 'These crusades have done more harm than good, I think. They have not won back Jerusalem, and many brave men have died of fever or wounds. Poor Philippe le Hardi, who died himself a year ago, had to watch his father handsome King Louis die of plague at Tunis. Philippe III was a king with no luck at all; in the end he was killed in the Spanish wars, in Aragon. I do not like his son, the new King of France: he is handsome also, but cruel.'

'Do not speak any more of sad things,' he said to her. 'Let us make love.'

She agreed, not unwillingly: he was charming and considerate, this older man: if she liked the country better the marriage itself would be very agreeable. Someone had told her that this King was so greatly beloved among his people that a man would hang himself if the King asked him to do so. That was perhaps going a little far; but Yolande smiled, and again

allowed Alexander to be her lover. He was to leave soon for
Edinburgh, for a council; but as usual promised to be with her
before morning if a storm should arise. It was probable, at this
time of year, that one might do so.

'It might be the Day of Judgement,' someone said, hearing the
wind.

The King threw back his head and laughed. They had
supped cheerfully together, this company of his lords and
himself; there had been a great deal of talk over the red wine of
Gascony he loved; he remembered drinking it at Dunfermline
long ago when someone had suggested Spens as a good
sea-captain, the best that ever sailed, fit to take young Margaret
to Norway. Why recall that now? The past was buried; soon he
would ride to Kinghorn in Fife, where Yolette was staying. It
would be necessary to do so because the wind was rising again,
hurling itself about the Castle Rock; she would hear it from
across the water. *I am afraid of storms. It is folly, but the way I am
made.* The way she was made still fascinated him; he would be
with her before morning. He would take a boat across the
Queen's Ferry where Margaret Atheling had landed long ago,
and then ride on. He knew he had lingered overlong, with the
good company and the good wine: men's talk together was
agreeable now and then, no doubt.

They begged him to stay, but he would not. Flushed and
happy, he ordered three knights to ride with him to the Ferry.
By the time they took horse there the storm had broken, and
rain and sleet hurled against their faces. It sobered Alexander:
and the night was dark, with no moon. More by luck than good
guidance, and already soaked to the skin, they reached the
Ferry at last. The boatman was loth to put out on such a night.

Alexander slapped the man on the shoulder; he was always at
home with the common folk. 'Why, friend, are you afeared to
face death in such company as myself?' With his height and his
bright hair, everyone in Scotland knew him for the King: and
although he himself knew that the wine had made him boastful,
the boatman answered respectfully.

'Not I, sire; it would well become me to perish with your
father's son.' The words were remembered afterwards.

His father. Alexander thought of that wise and much-tried
monarch as the boat struggled against the wind and high waves
of the Forth. It rocked, but they made the crossing. Margaret
Atheling herself had made it often enough. She must have

known many such storms, after the first of all that bore her to the coast of Scotland.

They reached the shore, and disembarked at Inverkeithing, seeing nothing, for the darkness, of the high triangular coast. Everything was shrouded in blackness, even the saltworks hard by the water; one would not have known they were there except for a single flickering lamp. The master of the works, on hearing that the King had come, ventured out himself into the storm, struggling against the wind to wrap his cloak about him. He had to shout to be heard against the elements.

'Sire, go no further on such a night! There is a bed in my house if you will accept it. Ride on in the morning, when light has come; it is madness to travel further in this dark, on a night made for devils and witches.'

The King laughed. They did not consider who was waiting for him, afraid of storms. 'No, no, good friend; having come safe so far, I will go on. Give me, I pray you, not a bed, but two men to walk by me as guides, for it is too dark to see as I ride.' The three knights had left him when he entered the boat.

He vaulted to the half-seen saddle; the horse was one he did not know. They must have gone two miles, battling always against the hail and wind, when they lost the track. The horse's hooves had begun to sink in underbrush of some kind, maybe heather; it grew thick here. The way lay along a narrow bridle path he had often enough followed, but the trees groaning in the hurricane told him nothing, he might be on moor or near forest, or not. He realised that he did not in fact know where he was; the guides also had lost direction. If only a light would shine to let him see the way! If Yolette would light her lamp in the distance! She must be sure he would come to her; it could not be far now, if one could only see: but the hail blinded him.

He thought of her, as he battled on. She might even be asleep by this; if so, he would astonish her by sliding into her bed, then together, locked close in one another's arms, they would listen to the storm beyond the walls. She would feel safe once he was with her: but the way was black ahead, the high wind shrieking.

The horse seemed baffled by the wind soon, losing the sixth sense horses have about where to avoid setting foot. The guides had lost themselves on the moor, if it was such; he could not now tell, and he would not wait for them.

He spurred the horse, thinking to leave matters to the animal's judgement: there was no other choice. The storm and wind howled on. There was nothing to be heard but that; not even the sound, presently, of falling stones at a cliff's edge. Above the sound of the wind came then, for seconds only, the terrified shriek of a horse as it fell into nothingness. There might also have been a man's last thought, a cry forever unheard: *Eheu, Scotia!* He had forgotten his kingdom in love's need; the only time in all his life that he had failed his country. There was silence after that except for the wind, and the wind tore on till morning.

They found the King dead on the beach next day, the dead horse by him. His neck was broken. They lifted the great limp handsome body carefully, and one man primmed his lips; this was God's vengeance, because the King had made merry in Lent on the very night men honour St. Joseph: and had left his wine to hasten to his French bride in her bed, at Kinghorn across the water.

It was only after prayers had been said, and masses sung for the dead man's soul, and a sorrowful pilgrimage made with the body to Dunfermline with a sad late Easter to come, that it was realised that there was now no king in Scotland, no heir unless Queen Yolande should by chance be expecting one. She was not. Except for a little child in Norway, her very existence hardly remembered at first by most, the line of Malcolm Ceann Mór had come to an end. The curse laid on the Athelings had been fulfilled: and Scotland lay leaderless except for a handful of guardians loyal to the late King, but none knowing by now who was their master. For the moment, it was agreed to rally to the symbol of the Lion; this was something the people would understand.

However fear and grief stalked the land. It was known that Thomas of Ercildoune, old now but remembered to have seen the Queen of Elfland and to have received the Sight from her, had prophesied King Alexander's death the day before it happened: and had said that there was worse to come.

This story began with a dead child, and should end with one; but there were many who did not acknowledge the claims of the little Maid of Norway, Alexander's grandchild, a foreigner and a girl. Among the dissenters were the Bruce clan, whom the dead King had named his heirs by default should any ill fate befall the child. They raided the Galloway castles which belonged to John Baliol, at Buittle and Wigtown, for John, a peaceable man, was descendant likewise of David of Huntingdon by another daughter and might claim the throne.

The Bruces prepared to stake their own claim, but others recognised the absent Maid herself as queen and agreed that she should be betrothed to the Prince of Wales, Edward's son born at last at Caernarvon. The Maid's widowed father King Eirik, who however owed King Edward money, was not anxious to send her overseas, young and helpless as she was; an English ship came for her laden with gingerbread and figs and other delights, and he would not put her aboard it. Later, when the treaty of betrothal was signed, the little girl, aged eight, was allowed to board a Scots ship, with a bishop and certain ladies in charge of her. She died between the Bishop's hands on Orkney, no one was certain why; seasickness does not kill, and it was in the interests of several that the child Queen should never reach Scotland. Her body was taken back to Norway, where her father caused the small coffin to be opened and identified the remains carefully. This was as well; a decade later, after Eirik's own death, a young woman appeared with her husband from Lübeck and claimed to be none other than Margaret, Queen of Scots. She was burned as an impostor at Bergen; sympathisers raised a church on the site. By then, the year 1301, Bruce himself was battling in Scotland against great odds; Edward of England had marched north, with his lieutenant John de Warenne of Surrey, and had removed the sacred Stone of Scone, the regalia, Margaret Atheling's Black Rood and Alexander II's sapphire, and taken them south in defiance of his own elected puppet Baliol, Surrey's son-in-law. He had burned Berwick and had done to death the great patriot William Wallace by a method of devising which may have been inspired by the witnessed mutilation of the body, after death, of Simon de Montfort long ago at Evesham. It was to be thirteen years of bitter war before Bruce himself, crowned long since with improvised regalia, cantered out at Bannockburn on

> *... ane gay palfrey,*
> *Litill and joly,*

and raised himself in the stirrups as de Bohun's great destrier thundered by, cleaving the English skull in two with his long-handled axe. 'It is a pity I have broken my good axe,' he remarked afterwards.

Later still, in a letter to the Pope from Arbroath, where the bones of the Lion lay, certain lines were to be read by His Holiness and to move him greatly enough to acknowledge Scotland, like his predecessor, as an independent kingdom.

... so long as a hundred of us remain alive, we will never submit to

the English ... it is not for glory, or riches, or honour that we fight, but for liberty, which no man lays down but with his life.

Scotland had remained a nation through adversity. She had become one by the courage and foresight of her early kings, by then long dead.

It is however uncertain how long an ill charm persists. After the Wars of Independence had been fiercely fought and won, it seemed to linger on in the Bruce descent, later the Stewart. King Robert's late-born son was sterile by two marriages, the first to England. His half-sister Marjory, imprisoned for eight years in the war, had been killed by a fall from her horse long since and had given birth then to a posthumous son by her young husband, Walter the Steward. Robert II was the first king of an ill-fated line dogged by misfortune, murder, death by accident, death in war again with England, the ever-watchful enemy; broken hearts, imprisonment, the scaffold, revolution and exile and the birth of heirs too late. By the lateral line which came then to inherit, a disease recurred which can be mistaken for madness. Perhaps the cycle completed itself in such ways by a contemptuous poet's line near the end:

An old, blind, mad, despised, and dying king.

Seven centuries had come and gone since Donald Bán, blind also, had worked in his laundry, full of hoarded vengeance to bequeath. A royal line seems no doubt more accursed than others; but perhaps it is merely that such things are recorded.

About the time of George III's supposed final madness, a descendant of the Scottish Kings, having inherited their poetry, had also inherited the ancient curse. His line would never breed sons to inherit from fathers; the fact had been noted in the family for generations. Lord Byron was therefore looking for a name for his unborn daughter. Nobly born and lame, he had been, and in a way still was by then, the lion of London society, but his marriage had been ill-considered and would soon end. However he looked forward to the child. The family's curse he thought had come from the time of the Dissolution of the Monasteries under Henry VIII, when Byron's ancestors had drunk wine from the skulls of disinterred monks at Newstead Abbey, his ancestral home in Nottinghamshire. Byron had suited his own fancy and had drunk wine himself from a skull at Newstead earlier in his career, but had had it bordered with silver first. If this child was a girl, he knew what he would call her ... *it is an antique title not used since the time of King John.* He had found the name either by ferreting about among his family papers, or else from the not too accurate recollections of his deceased Scots mother: he could not recall which. At any rate it was a pleasant name: Ada. He hoped no ill fortune would befall her, but perhaps after all it would be a son.

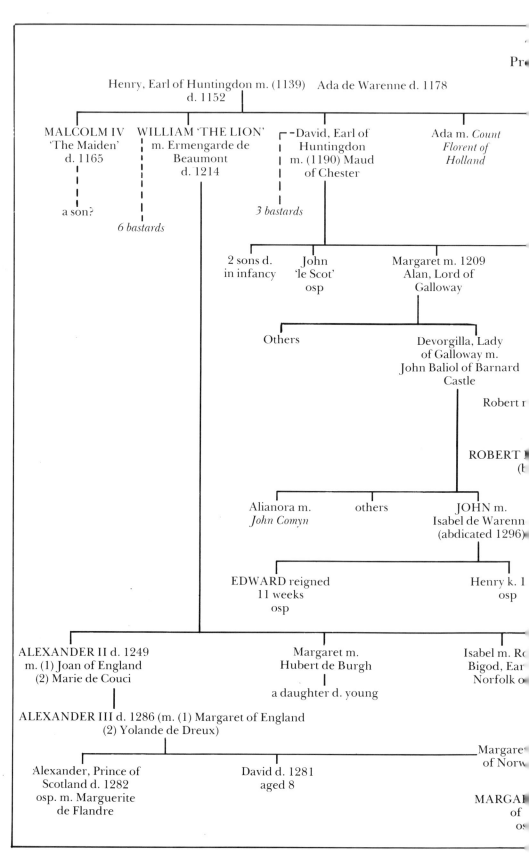

Henry, Earl of Huntingdon m. (1139)   Ada de Warenne d. 1178
d. 1152

MALCOLM IV   WILLIAM 'THE LION'   David, Earl of   Ada m. *Count*
'The Maiden'   m. Ermengarde de   Huntingdon   *Florent of*
d. 1165   Beaumont   m. (1190) Maud   *Holland*
                     d. 1214   of Chester

a son?   *3 bastards*

            6 bastards

                              2 sons d.   John   Margaret m. 1209
                              in infancy   'le Scot'   Alan, Lord of
                                             osp   Galloway

                                   Others   Devorgilla, Lady
                                                            of Galloway m.
                                                            John Baliol of Barnard
                                                            Castle

                                                                      Robert r

                                                            ROBERT I
                                                                     (b

                              Alianora m.   others   JOHN m.
                              John Comyn   Isabel de Warenn
                                                            (abdicated 1296)

                                   EDWARD reigned   Henry k. 1
                                   11 weeks   osp
                                   osp

ALEXANDER II d. 1249   Margaret m.   Isabel m. R
m. (1) Joan of England   Hubert de Burgh   Bigod, Ear
(2) Marie de Couci   Norfolk o
                                             a daughter d. young

ALEXANDER III d. 1286 (m. (1) Margaret of England
(2) Yolande de Dreux)
                                                                     Margare
                                                                     of Norw

Alexander, Prince of   David d. 1281
Scotland d. 1282   aged 8   MARGAI
osp. m. Marguerite   of
de Flandre   os

KEY
Kings of Scots in capitals
Pretenders outlined
Bastard lines dotted
Competitors in 1291 in italics

la d. 1152
osp

Margaret m. Duke
Conan IV
of Brittany

Constance m.
(1) Geoffrey Plantagenet

Eleanor osp

Arthur
murdered 1203

Ada m. Henry
de Hastynges

John

Descent from Alfred the Great (simplified)

ETHELRED II Unred m. (2) ⟶ Emma of Normandy
by a first wife

Edmund Ironside

Alfred
k. 1036
osp

Edward the
Confessor
d. 1066
osp

Edward the Stranger
m. (?) Agatha of Hungary

Carrick

wned 1306
s)

Margaret m.
Malcolm III

Christina
(abbess)

Edgar the
Atheling osp

Marjory k.
1316 m. Walter the
High Steward

ROBERT II

THE STEWART KINGS
OF SCOTLAND

Marjory m. Gilbert Earl
of Pembroke
osp

id